THE CRANIUM OF THE NEWBORN INFANT

An ATLAS of Tomography and Anatomical Sections

Robert H. Pierce M.D.

Michael W. Mainen M.D.

James F. Bosma M.D.

Illustrated by:

Keiko Hiratsuka Moore

Howard C. Bartner

George P. Marsden

CHP

Castle House Publications Ltd.

ISBN 0 7194 0009 0

1979 Castle House Publications Ltd.

Preface

This project, sponsored by the National Institute of Dental Research, was generated by the association within the Clinical Center, National Institutes of Health, of Robert H. Pierce, a Clinical Associate in the Diagnostic Radiology Department, of Michael W. Mainen, a Clinical Associate in the National Institute of Dental Research, and James F. Bosma, of the NIDR Section on Oral and Pharyngeal Development. To this association, Robert Pierce brought an interest in tomography acquired as a protege of Galdino E. Valvassori, of the Department of Radiology, University of Illinois Eye and Ear Infirmary. In some respects, this study is a sequel and analogue of *The Interpretation of Tomograms of the Head, An Atlas* by M. L. Daves and E. Loechel (1962), which was also produced intramurally at the National Institutes of Health.

Acknowledgments

Appreciation is expressed to the various individuals and organizations whose assistance has made this project possible. The specimens of infant crania were selected from the collection in the University of Maryland Department of Anatomy, by the arrangement of Frank Figge, and from the collection of the National Biological Laboratory, by arrangement of George Halpin.

The figures and text have been reviewed at considerable effort by Galdino E. Valvassori, of the Department of Radiology, University of Illinois (Chicago) College of Medicine, by Frederick N. Silverman, of the Division of Radiology, Children's Hospital Medical Center, Cincinnati, by Edmund S. Crelin and E. Leon Kier, of the Human Growth and Development Study Unit and the Division of Neuroradiology, Department of Diagnostic Radiology, respectively, Yale University School of Medicine.

Table of Contents

List of Illustrations

Chapter 5

Chapter 6

CHAPTER 1

Introduction

The cranium develops as a composite of bones which differ in embryologic origin and in mechanisms and patterns of growth and modulation of form. The BASIOCCIPITAL, EXOCCIPITAL, a portion of the SUPRAOCCIPITAL, the BASISPHENOID, PETROSAL and ETHMOID are preformed in cartilage. Growth of the BASISPHENOID, BASIOCCIPITAL, EXOCCIPITAL and the chondral portion of the SUPRAOCCIPITAL is principally at their cartilaginous synchondroses, until the cartilage is replaced by bone and bony fusion occurs. Thereafter, growth is only at their periosteal margins.

The cartilage skeleton of the branchial arches is the origin of the auditory ossicles and the styloid process.

Most of the cranial bones are membranous in derivation. The squamous elements enclosing the brain case, or calvarium, include the ALISPHENOID, the FRONTAL, the SQUAMOSAL and a portion of the SUPRAOCCIPITAL. These bones ossify peripheralward from one or a few centers within membrane units. Growth continues in irregular distribution, alternating with erosion, at most of their sutural approximations, so that they become interdigitated. They are further modulated in form by apposition or resorption at their inner and outer periosteal surfaces. And, like the rest of the skeleton, their internal trabecular arrangement is continuously adapted to physical stress.

Of the membranous bones of the face, the NASAL and LACRIMAL are initially formed and later shaped in manner like the squamous bones of the calvarium. The MAXILLA, PALATINE and MALAR are formed from multiple ossification centers, but late in fetal life become a single bone. These major facial bones, and the MANDIBLE, undergo extensive growth and modulation of form during fetal and postnatal development.

The external margins of the head, and of its oral and pharyngeal cavities, are smoothly contoured and these contours change subtly during fetal and postnatal development. But the components of the cranium change markedly in structure, in their relative size, in their spatial orientation and in the patterns of sutural approximation. The teeth are also in developmental progression.

Radiography, and tomography in particular, give us strategic information about these sequential developments. The radiographic criteria are multiplied by the differences in skeletal structure. Cartilage is conspicuously radiolucent. The cancellous matrix of ossified bones is less radiopaque than the cortex. The paranasal and paratympanic air cells are lucent, and margined with radiopaque cortex. But the auditory ossicles and the ANNULUS remain relatively dense and radiopaque. The bony labyrinth, of distinctive non-trabecular bone, and the adjacent bone of the petrous pyramid are distinctively dense. Radiographically, the tooth buds afford a variety of criteria, including the radiodense enamel, the less dense dentin and the denser margin of the crypt.

This multiplicity of radiographic criteria gives opportunity for greater discrimination of skeletal development in the cranium than in the limbs and trunk. But, at the present time, we are still largely dependent upon calibrations of development derived from standardized radiography of dental maturation and skeletal epiphyseal maturation in the limbs and/or the trunk. The variety of skeletal changes in the cranium should be calibrated in relation to these other criteria of development.

Such comparisons are needed to distinguish the relative contribution of systemic factors vis-a-vis local determinants of growth and development in the cranium. The calvarium grows and develops rapidly in fetal life in correlation with the rapid growth of the brain. Criteria taken from the OCCIPITAL, SPHENOID and TEMPORAL composites are particularly relevant to development of the brain stem. The facial skeleton grows and develops in correlation with enlargement of the pharynx and the nasal and oral chambers. The development of the portion of the cranium related to the cervical vertebrae and cervical musculature corresponds in general with that of the skeleton of the trunk.

Parallel evaluation of the cranium and of other parts of the skeleton is, at the present time, the basis for the clinical distinction of generalized skeletal disorders from cranial abnormalities. Dyschondroplasia, for instance, is clinically more familiar in the limbs and trunk than in the cranium. But the dyschondroplasias which result in the cranial distortions described by Crouzon and by Apert occur exclusively or principally in the chondrocranium. Likewise, systemic abnormalities of the bony skeleton, such as nephropathic and hypovitaminotic rickets are better defined outside of the head. But metaphysial, or craniometaphysial, dysplasia (Pyle), a failure of the osteoclastic element of modulation of form, is best detected in the cranium. Likewise, the skeletal correlates of hemolytic and iron deficiency anemias may first be recognized in the cranium. The hyperostosis of hypervitaminosis A and the lytic lesions of Gaucher's disorder may selectivity involve the skull. Neoplastic lesions, such as leukemic infiltrations or the metastases of sarcoma may appear initially in the skull.

The cranium is of particular clinical significance as it evidences regional disorders. These disorders are as varied as the developmental components of the head. The brain is liable to the greatest variety of developmental abnormalities. Some of the skeletal reflections of brain disorders are seemingly simple. For instance, the calvarium expands about a meningeal chamber which is abnormally expanded by hydrocephaly or macrocephaly. Reciprocally, microcephaly is associated with microcranium, selectively involving the calvarium. But the distortions of the cranium associated with certain patterns of brain hypoplasia may be more complex. Thus, in "anencephaly" a bifid and hypoplastic brain is only partially enclosed by a markedly hypoplastic calvarium. But the more caudal skeleton, particularly that of the upper extremities, may be overgrown. Nañagas (1925) interprets this juxtaposition of hyperplasia to abnormal hypoplasia as evidence of the caudalward displacement of the cephalic instigation of growth.

Most of the developmental distortions of the facial portion of the cranium are a part of regional abnormalities as arrhinencephaly, or hypoplasia of the eye, or cleft of the palate and/or lip. These are initiated in embryo, and the mesenchyme generating the skeleton participates in the regional disruption. In this process, the variations of the embryonic neural and epithelial elements are probably determinant. Developmental distortions of the rhinencephalon are associated with severe and peculiar distortions of the facial skeleton. In severe arrhinencephaly, with absence of the olfactory apparatus, the nose is hypoplastic or absent and the face develops in relevance to the eyes, mouth and pharynx. In the circumstance of primary hypoplasia of the eyes, the skeletal orbits are small and abnormally shaped. The skeletal abnormalities of cleft palate and/or cleft lip extend to a variable degree and in variable direction to the nasal, orbital and basilar portions of the cranium, to the mandible and to the upper cervical vertebrae.

Those abnormalities which are associated with motor impairment each influence skeletal development in specific and characteristic manner. In primary disorders of the motor unit, the individual's pattern of muscular hypoplasia and fibrosis is associated with hypoplasia and deformation of the skeleton to which the musculature is attached. Analogous skeletal deformation results if the central neurological lesion results in atony. Other patterns of skeletal deformation result if the neurological lesion results in a spastic form of dyskinesia.

In summary, the heterogenously derived cranium is the site of expression of a variety of skeletal disorders, some of which are restricted to this region. The cranium is also the site of expression of a larger variety of regional abnormalities, primary in brain and/or the peripheral innervation including the nose, eye and ear. More incidentally, certain portions of the cranium may evidence disorders which are principally of the motor system. This heterogeneity must be kept in mind as the clinician selects radiographic procedures to elucidate a particular "congenital abnormality" of the head.

This heterogeneity of patterns of abnormalities involving the cranium is being elucidated by clinical experience. It is appropriate to mention the strategic significance of postmortem radiographic and anatomic studies in the circumstance of death of an infant who has demonstrable abnormality of the cranium. Extensive radiographic studies, followed by anatomical dissection, will advance our understanding of these abnormalities.

CHAPTER 2

Material & Procedures

These demonstrations are of portions of 4 crania selected from 25 late fetal or early infantile specimens. Seven of these specimen crania were obtained from the collection of the Department of Anatomy, University of Maryland School of Medicine, from a racially varied population. Eighteen crania were selected from the large stock of the National Biological Supply Company, which had been obtained from sources of India. The specimens from each of these sources were of unidentified subjects, without information about gestational or postnatal age, details of birth, clinical circumstance of death or measurements of the cadaver. Mandibles were included, but no other portions of the skeleton were available.

But, in common with most specimen infant crania, these had undergone postmortem distortion in form and general dimension. Accordingly, qualitative criteria, rather than measurements, were employed for estimation of developmental status. The crania from the commercial laboratory were prepared in routine manner by manual cleaning of detritus and by the spray application of a thin plastic covering. The crania from the Department of Anatomy were manually cleaned and were, in general, anatomically more complete. In most of the crania, the tympanic membranes were complete or nearly complete. Consistently among these specimen crania, the tympanic membrane, MALLEUS and INCUS were retracted from the position in which they are found in infant cadavers or in most living infants.

Specifically, in approximately a diminishing order of significance, our externally evident criteria of gestational term status were:

In the PETROSAL—The carotid canal is enclosed inferiorly. The fossa of the geniculate ganglion is nearly closed. The subarcuate fossa is partially closed at its orifice. The internal acoustic meatus is approximately 5–5½ mm. deep. The petrosquamosal suture is firmly closed by bony approximation,

without fusion in its length in the tegmen.

The anterior and posterior portions of the ANNULUS are approximated; it has extended medialward, along the inferior aspect of the PETROSAL, and lateralward, along the superior and anterior aspect of the external auditory canal.

In the BASISPHENOID, the anterior clinoid processes incompletely approximate the midline. The dorsum sellae and the posterior clinoid processes are entirely chondral. The PTERYGOID is visibly fused or nearly fused with the medial pterygoid process.

In the FRONTAL, the roof of the orbit is continuous. The supraorbital fissure is open within the supraorbital ridge.

In the SQUAMOSAL, the mandibular fossa is only slightly concave.

In the PALATINE, the posterior margin of the bony palate is slightly indented or is straight across the midline; there is no posterior nasal spine.

In the MAXILLA, the length of the infraorbital canal is open to the orbit or, in some specimens, it may be enclosed at its anterior orifice. The anterior nasal spine is a distinct prominence.

In the SUPRAOCCIPITAL, the suture between its chondral and membranous portions is open only in its lateral portion.

The posterior margin of the VOMER approximates the anterior-inferior angle of the BASISPHENOID, immediately adjacent to the rostrum.

Radiological Procedures:

The selected crania, with the upper portion of the calvarium removed, were fixed upon ⅜″ (9½ mm) clear plastic by a layer of red orthodontic wax. The cranium rested on the occipital condyles and the margin of the maxillary alveolar ridge. Variably in individual crania, the inferior margin of the tympanic ring approximated this plane. In this position, a line between "basion" and "anterior nasal spine" parallels the surface of the mount.

The tomograms in the coronal and transverse plane were made on a North American Phillips Polytome. A hypocycloidal pattern of tube and cassette motions was utilized with a standard six second sweep 281 cm in length. The depth of focus with this apparatus is 1.2 mm. The peak kilovoltage and milliamperage varied with the specimen under examination. The coronal tomoradiographic sections of Chapter 4 were made at intervals of 5.0 mm anterior to the posterior clinoid processes and at 1.0 mm more posteriorly, to the middle of the foramen magnum. The transverse sections of Chapter 5 were at 1.0 mm intervals. The most inferior section (Figure 5.6) is through the maxillary teeth, the EXOCCIPITAL and the inferior portion of the pterygoid processes and the inferior portion of the PETROSAL. The most superior section is through the orbitosphenoid, the arcuate eminence of the PETROSAL and the superior portion of the nasal chamber.

The sagittal sections of the otic region skeleton (Chapter 6) were made on a Profexray Gyrotome. The tube and cassette were moved in circular pattern with a 3 second exposure. The kilovoltage and milliamperage were varied according to the specimen. Tomoradiographic sections were made at 1.0 mm intervals.

Anatomical Procedures

Following tomography, the calvarium was removed from the cranium and all periosteum and dura were stripped from the bones. Each tomogram was examined for visible features which were sufficiently discrete to define the plane of the section. In some tomograms, a single anatomical detail sufficed to identify a plane; in others, two or more less defined landmarks were required. When the locations of the tomograms were established, these were marked on full-sized photographs of the skull.

The cranium was coated lightly with wax and fixed in a rectangular wooden box. The anterior portion of the cranium selected for coronal sections was embedded in red acrylic, mixed in thin consistency. The mixture of embedding medium was first poured about the periphery of the cranium and then the orbits and the cranial vault were filled. The mass was extensively vibrated so that all accessible interstices were filled.

The selected lines of section, marked at intervals of 5 mm on the cranium, were extended as lines upon the enclosing box. The box, block and cranium were then cut by a band saw.

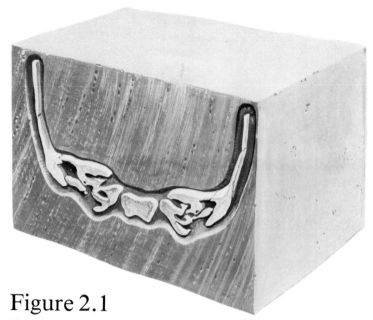

Figure 2.1

Drawing of cranium section embedded in stone. The matrix has been excavated to further expose the specimen.

The portion of this cranium posterior to the posterior clinoid processes was embedded in yellow dental stone. The cranium, in its stone block, was sawn through the posterior portion of foramen magnum. It was then sanded in the coronal plane, in an anteriorward sequence, in 1 mm. gradations. Sanding was done with a motor-driven dental model cutter: a water-cooled rotating abrasive disc which is approximated by the specimen block sliding under manual control on a fixed platform. The stone block provided good mechanical control of the specimen and helped in maintaining stable orientation. As the sanding progressed, the landmarks were sought which identified tomographic sections. The embedding materiel was excavated about the bone on the face of the cut which was to be drawn (See Fig. 2.1). Thus, the anatomical illustrations become somewhat three dimensional, demonstrating the bony anatomy in depth. But this technique of demonstration has resulted in the loss of certain anatomical details, such as the scroll-like portions of the nasal turbinals. The coronal sections of skeleton were prepared and drawn from caudal perspective. The cranium studied in transverse plane was embedded in yellow dental stone. The stone block and the cranium were then sanded in transverse plane, in an inferior-superior sequence. Correspondingly, the successive anatomical illustrations are from inferior perspective.

The crania demonstrated in coronal and in transverse sections were each slightly asymmetrical in relation to the plane of section. These slight asymmetries, estimated at 0.5 to 1.0 mm., were shown in sawn or ground sections and are noted in the comments accompanying the section illustrations. Fortunately, they often demonstrate additional anatomical information.

The cranium selected for sagittal sectional demonstration of the ear area was sawn in the midline and then coronally through the curve of the ALISPHENOID, slightly anterior to the round foramen, and coronally through the EXOCCIPITAL, posterior to the condyloid canal. The block was imbedded in the dental stone, leaving the median section plane slightly exposed. With this plane for orientation, the block and specimen were sanded in a medialward succession, approximating the tomograms at 1. mm intervals, beginning at the head of the MALLEUS and the body of the INCUS.

Relating of Tomographic and Anatomic Sections. The "matching" of radiographic and sawn or sanded anatomic sections offered problems because of the basic differences in the method and anatomic content of demonstration. The radiographic tomograms demonstrate a "slice" or section of significant diameter, with diminishing discrimination of anatomic elements on either side of this. Whereas the anatomic sections are a surface. infinitely thin, except as its margins adjacent to the section are exposed by excavation of the embedding matrix. Thus, relatively lucent structures such as dental crypts or buds, or the various parts of the labyrinth, are often better shown in the tomograms. The sutures which are in cross-wise orientation to the tomographic section are more evident radiographically than in the anatomical section, particularly if the suture is partially fused.

Procedures of Illustrations and Descriptions

The general radiographs and the tomograms were masked at the image margins. They were then logetronically intensified at a variety of discrimination selections and film developing procedures for optimal demonstration of selected details such as foramena, ossicles or elements of the labyrinth within the PETROSAL.

The reference figures of the tomograms consist of line tracings and cut-outs of the radiodense areas in partially opaque overlay sheets.

The drawings of these sections are precisely scaled.

In drawing the initial sections, a projection and grid system was employed. Subsequently, the artists depended upon multiple caliper measurements. All sections were drawn in magnification $\times$ 2. Drawings of the coronal and sagittal sections, of Chapters 4 and 6 respectively, are printed at this size. Drawings of the transverse sections, of Chapter 5, are printed at ¼ reduction; accordingly, these reproductions are at magnification $\times$ 1½.

The *terminology* is that of the Third Edition (1968) of the *Nomina Anatomica* partially adapted toward common vernacular. Bones which are unfused at gestational term are separately designated, using designations which are established in developmental anatomy. Thus, the separate components of the TEMPORAL are named the PETROSAL, SQUAMOSAL and ANNULUS. The OCCIPITAL is composed of the BASIOCCIPITAL, EXOCCIPITAL and SUPRAOCCIPITAL. The SPHENOID consists of the BASISPHENOID, ALISPHENOID, PTERYGOID and, inconstantly, the BONES of BERTIN. The PREMAXILLA is demarcated from the MAXILLA. The INFERIOR TURBINATE is demarcated from the ETHMOID. These separate bones are listed in the Anatomical Index under their general confluence and also singly.

The separate bones are consistently printed in small capitals.

The terms of spatial orientation and direction are interpolated from the mature human, as if the fetus were empirically gifted with the ability to stand in "anatomical position." This usage is incongruous, but it is an empiricism which is essential for effective communication with persons oriented to the anatomy of the mature human.

Descriptions of these specimens are in comparison with the anatomical studies of the cranium of the human fetus, term neonate and infant by Crelin (1969), Elias (1971), and in a *Symposium on Development of the Basicranium* (1976). And in comparison with the radiographic descriptions of the cranium of the normal human infant by Caffey (1973), Berkvens (1950), Chusler (1972) and Krogman and Chung (1965).

The cranium of the infant has not been described previously in sectional anatomy or in radiographic tomography. But tomography of the adult human cranium, particularly of the temporal area, has been comprehensively illustrated and described by Holvey, Rosenthal and Anson (1945), Petersen and Stoksted (1951), Fischgold, David and Bregeat (1952), Francois and Barrois (1952), Brunner, Petersen and Stoksted (1961), Daves and Loechel (1962), Valvassori (1963), Potter (1971), Binet and Moro (1972), and by Bennett, Brunner and Valvassori (1973).

It is anticipated that the tomographic techniques employes in these studies will be displaced by the techniques of computerized axial tomography which are now becoming available. These new methods, recently reviewed by Ledley *et al* (1974), Gordon *et al* (1975), New and Scott (1975), Robinson (1975), Prewitt (1976) and Webber (1976) effect superior anatomical demonstration with significant economy of radiation. The anatomical portion of this atlas is, thus, a reference in anticipation of these further advances.

Figure 2.2

Schematics of cranium with indications of anatomic directions and planes.
A. In frontal view
B. In lateral view

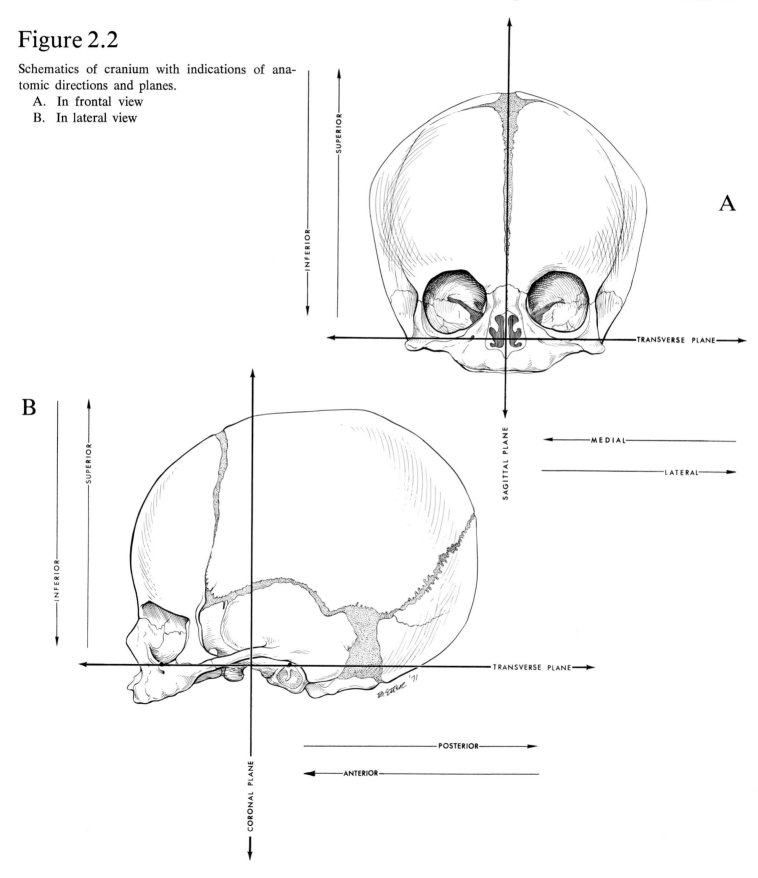

6

Drawings of Reference Cranium

This is the reference cranium of our project study. It is estimated at approximately term gestation by most of the criteria noted in Chapter 2.

Figure 3.1

Drawing, frontal view

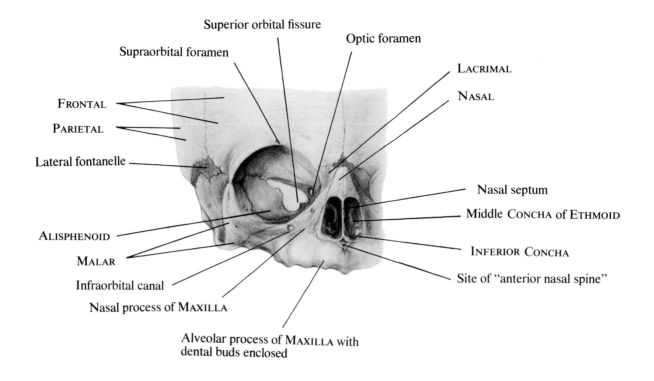

Superior orbital fissure

Optic foramen

Supraorbital foramen

LACRIMAL

NASAL

FRONTAL

PARIETAL

Lateral fontanelle

Nasal septum

Middle CONCHA of ETHMOID

ALISPHENOID

INFERIOR CONCHA

MALAR

Site of "anterior nasal spine"

Infraorbital canal

Nasal process of MAXILLA

Alveolar process of MAXILLA with
dental buds enclosed

Figure 3.2

Drawing, lateral view, and matching photograph

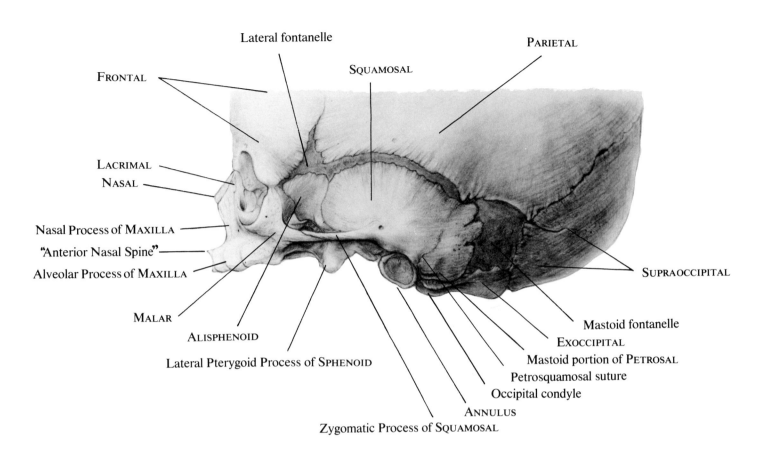

Lateral fontanelle

PARIETAL

SQUAMOSAL

FRONTAL

LACRIMAL

NASAL

Nasal Process of MAXILLA

"Anterior Nasal Spine"

Alveolar Process of MAXILLA

SUPRAOCCIPITAL

MALAR

ALISPHENOID

Mastoid fontanelle

EXOCCIPITAL

Lateral Pterygoid Process of SPHENOID

Mastoid portion of PETROSAL

Petrosquamosal suture

Occipital condyle

ANNULUS

Zygomatic Process of SQUAMOSAL

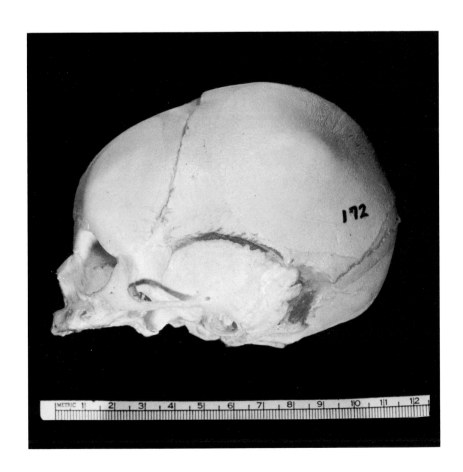

9

Figure 3.3

Drawing, superior view, roof of calvarium removed

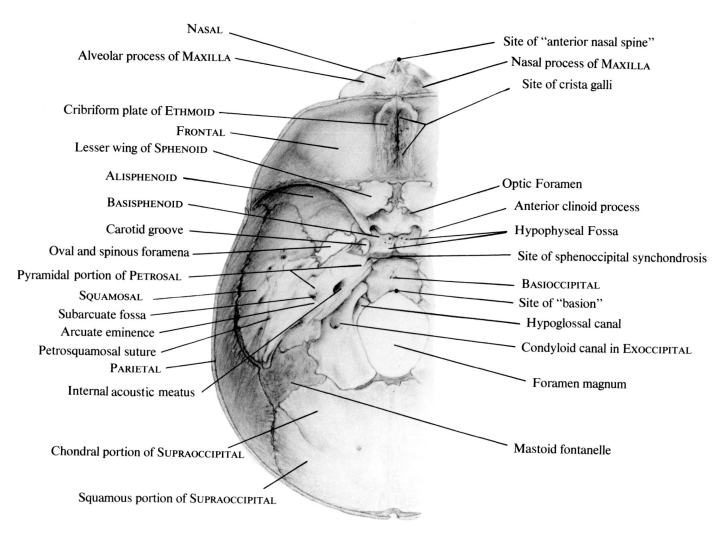

NASAL

Alveolar process of MAXILLA

Site of "anterior nasal spine"

Nasal process of MAXILLA

Site of crista galli

Cribriform plate of ETHMOID

FRONTAL

Lesser wing of SPHENOID

ALISPHENOID

BASISPHENOID

Carotid groove

Oval and spinous foramena

Pyramidal portion of PETROSAL

SQUAMOSAL

Subarcuate fossa

Arcuate eminence

Petrosquamosal suture

PARIETAL

Internal acoustic meatus

Chondral portion of SUPRAOCCIPITAL

Squamous portion of SUPRAOCCIPITAL

Optic Foramen

Anterior clinoid process

Hypophyseal Fossa

Site of sphenoccipital synchondrosis

BASIOCCIPITAL

Site of "basion"

Hypoglossal canal

Condyloid canal in EXOCCIPITAL

Foramen magnum

Mastoid fontanelle

Figure 3.4

Drawing, inferior view, and matching photograph

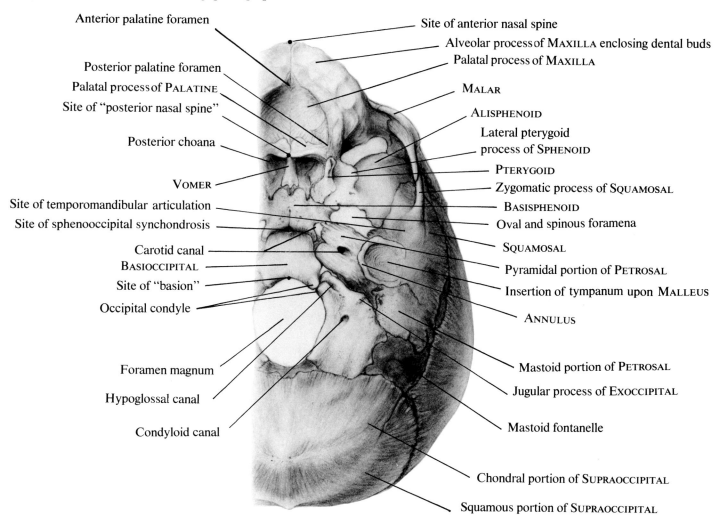

Anterior palatine foramen
Posterior palatine foramen
Palatal process of PALATINE
Site of "posterior nasal spine"
Posterior choana
VOMER
Site of temporomandibular articulation
Site of sphenooccipital synchondrosis
Carotid canal
BASIOCCIPITAL
Site of "basion"
Occipital condyle
Foramen magnum
Hypoglossal canal
Condyloid canal

Site of anterior nasal spine
Alveolar process of MAXILLA enclosing dental buds
Palatal process of MAXILLA
MALAR
ALISPHENOID
Lateral pterygoid process of SPHENOID
PTERYGOID
Zygomatic process of SQUAMOSAL
BASISPHENOID
Oval and spinous foramena
SQUAMOSAL
Pyramidal portion of PETROSAL
Insertion of tympanum upon MALLEUS
ANNULUS
Mastoid portion of PETROSAL
Jugular process of EXOCCIPITAL
Mastoid fontanelle
Chondral portion of SUPRAOCCIPITAL
Squamous portion of SUPRAOCCIPITAL

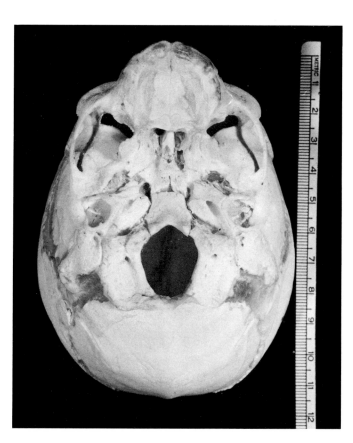

CHAPTER 4

Coronal Tomograms and Drawn Sections

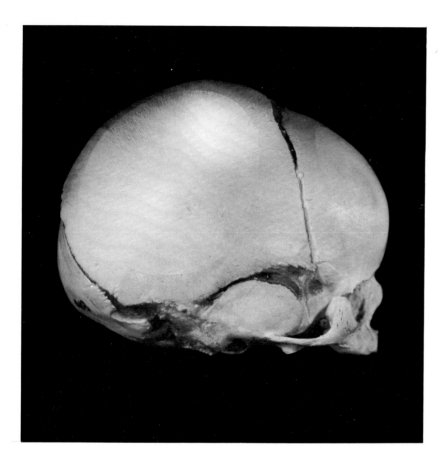

Figure 4.1
Photograph of cranium, lateral view

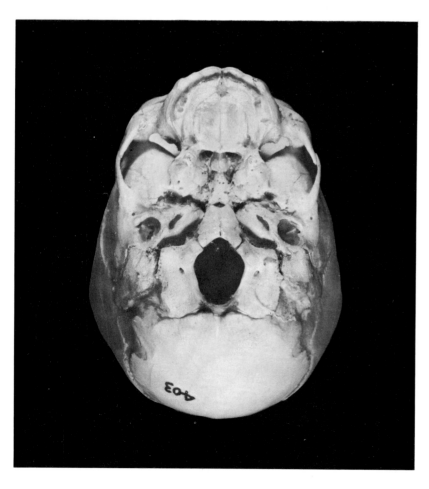

Figure 4.3
Photograph of cranium, inferior view

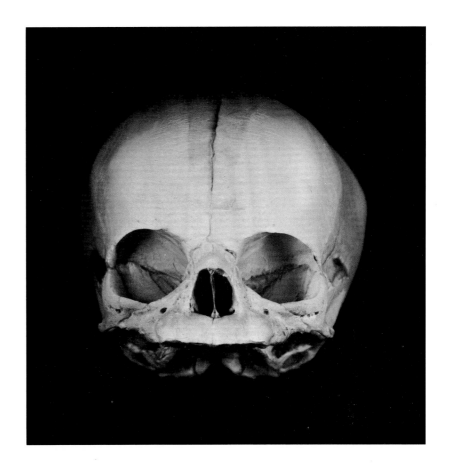

Figure 4.2

Photograph of cranium, frontal view

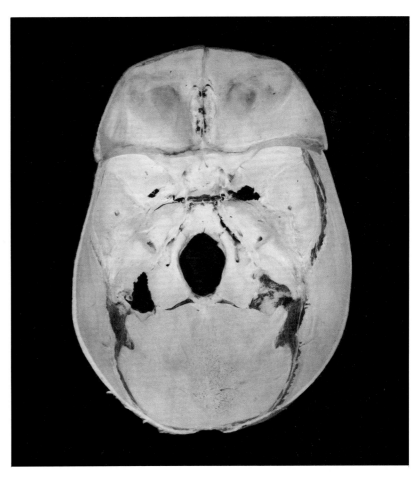

Figure 4.4

Photograph of cranium, superior view, roof of calvarium removed

Figure 4.5   Orientation of Sections

—on superior aspect of cranium, roof of calvarium removed
—on inferior aspect of cranium

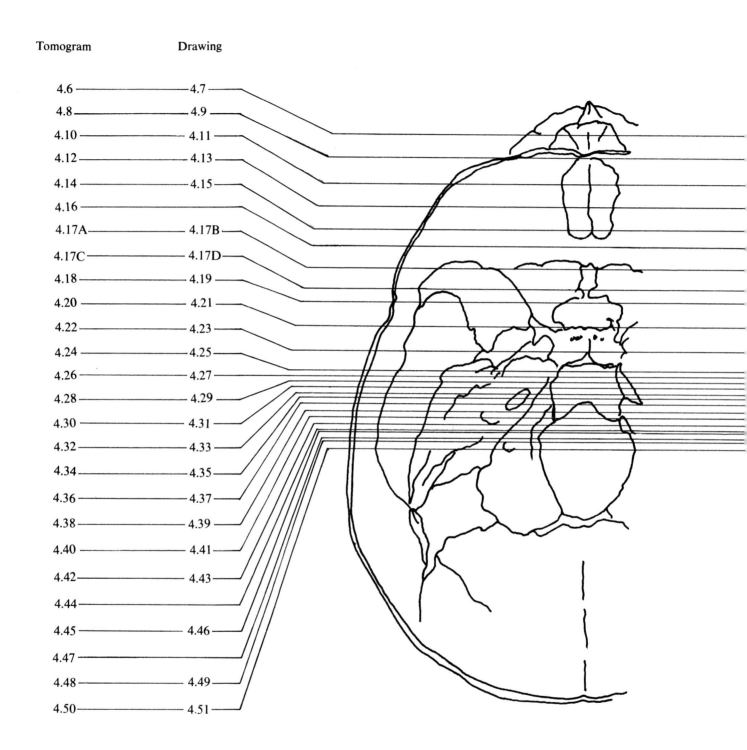

Tomogram

Drawing

4.6	4.7
4.8	4.9
4.10	4.11
4.12	4.13
4.14	4.15
4.16	
4.17A	4.17B
4.17C	4.17D
4.18	4.19
4.20	4.21
4.22	4.23
4.24	4.25
4.26	4.27
4.28	4.29
4.30	4.31
4.32	4.33
4.34	4.35
4.36	4.37
4.38	4.39
4.40	4.41
4.42	4.43
4.44	
4.45	4.46
4.47	
4.48	4.49
4.50	4.51

SUPERIOR ASPECT

16

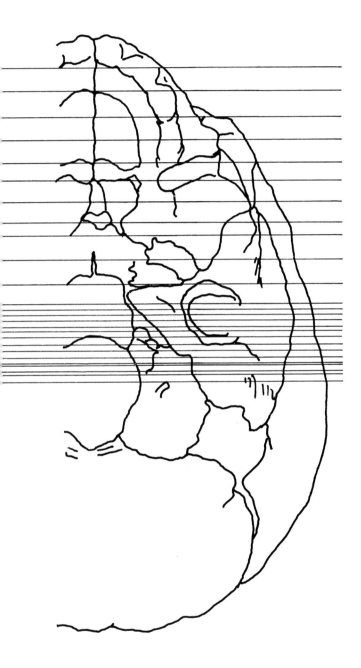

INFERIOR ASPECT

Figure 4.6*

Tomogram   Drawing

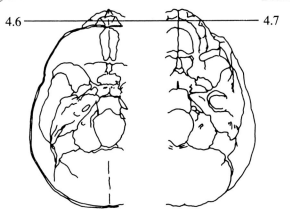

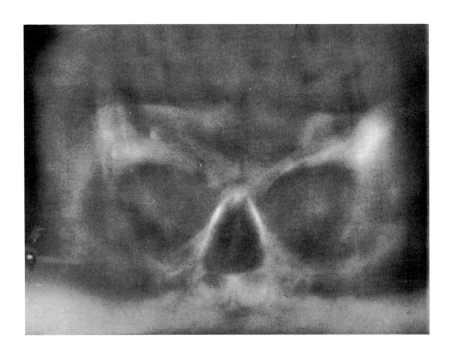

This tomogram corresponds with the anatomical section of Figure 4.7. The LATERAL INCISOR in its crypt is seen indistinctly on each side.
The interfrontal and the frontonasal sutures are distinct.

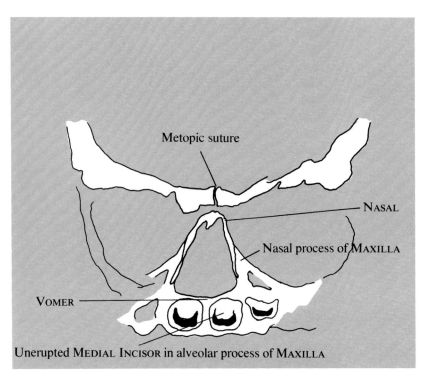

Metopic suture

NASAL

Nasal process of MAXILLA

VOMER

Unerupted MEDIAL INCISOR in alveolar process of MAXILLA

*Tomograms were taken of the cranium at 5 mm. intervals from the anterior plane of the MEDIAL DECIDUAL INCISORs (Fig. 4.6) to that of the posterior margin of the bony palate (Fig. 4.22). The cranium mounted in plaster was sawn at 5 mm. intervals corresponding to the tomographic plane (Fig. 4.7 to 4.23).

The tomograms and drawn sections are presented here in anterior to posterior sequence. All drawings are from posterior view.

18

Figure 4.7

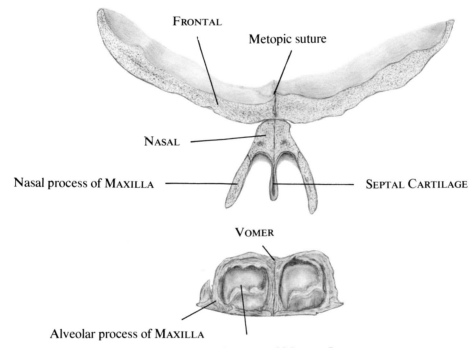

FRONTAL

Metopic suture

NASAL

Nasal process of MAXILLA

SEPTAL CARTILAGE

VOMER

Alveolar process of MAXILLA

Unerupted MEDIAL INCISOR

This is the most anterior coronal anatomical section. It includes a portion of the alveolar process of the MAXILLA. The posterior margins of the DECIDUAL MEDIAL INCISOR crypts are open.

The bony skeleton of the external nose sectioned through the NASALs and through the nasal process of the MAXILLA. The FRONTALS are sectioned at the base of the frontal eminence.

Figure 4.8

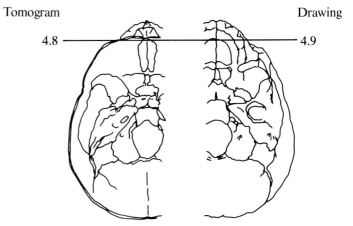

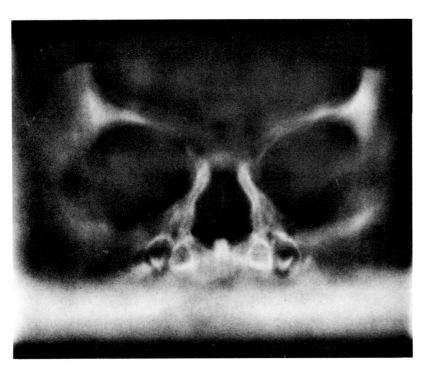

This tomogram demonstrates structures 5 mm posterior to those of Figure 4.6. The crypt and bud of the CUSPID are distinct on each side.

The nasolacrimal canal is shown in much of its length.

The VOMER is shown as paramedian plates which are not demarcated from the ETHMOID or the MAXILLA.

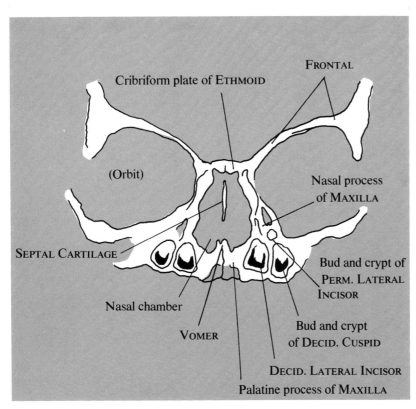

Figure 4.9

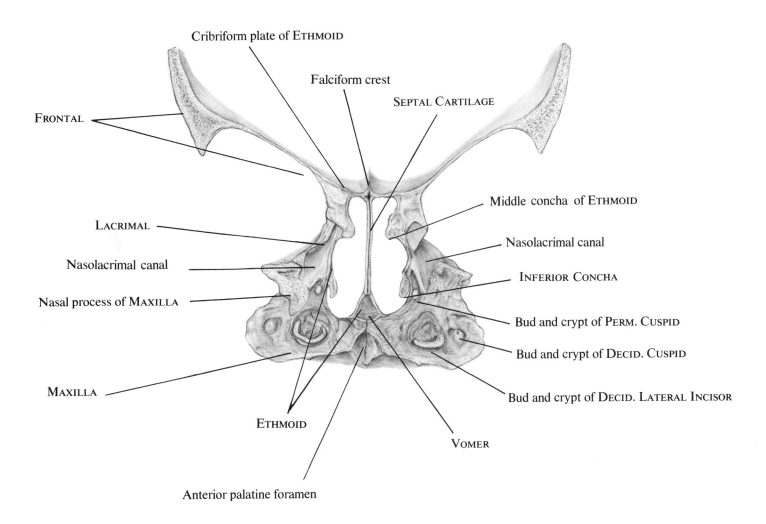

Cribriform plate of ETHMOID

Falciform crest

SEPTAL CARTILAGE

FRONTAL

Middle concha of ETHMOID

LACRIMAL

Nasolacrimal canal

Nasolacrimal canal

INFERIOR CONCHA

Nasal process of MAXILLA

Bud and crypt of PERM. CUSPID

Bud and crypt of DECID. CUSPID

MAXILLA

Bud and crypt of DECID. LATERAL INCISOR

ETHMOID

VOMER

Anterior palatine foramen

The MAXILLA is sectioned on each side through the buds and crypts of the DECIDUAL LATERAL INCISOR and CUSPID and of the PERMANENT CUSPID. Its nasal process extends lateral to the LACRIMAL. The anterior palatine foramen is prominent.

On the right, both lateral and medial walls of the nasolacrimal canal are shown. On the left, the LACRIMAL is sectioned farther anteriorly, and only the medial wall of the canal is shown.

The FRONTAL is sectioned through the roof of the orbit immediately anterior to the perforated portion of the cribriform plate.

The anterior tip of the VOMER is seen as a symmetrical thin plate, approximately transverse in orientation.

The ETHMOID is a continuous thin plate enclosing the nasal chamber laterally and superiorly and protruding into the chamber as the middle and superior conchae. The INFERIOR CONCHA is a bone of separate origin (the suture between the INFERIOR CONCHA and the ETHMOID is shown on the right). The SEPTAL CARTILAGE is commonly considered a separate entity; in the infant, it is ossified only at its superior margin. The crista galli is also part of the ETHMOID.

Figure 4.10

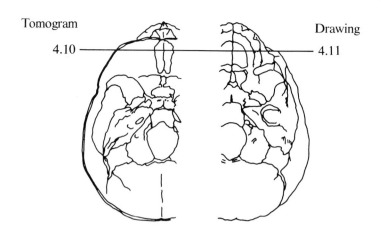

4.10 —————————————————— 4.11

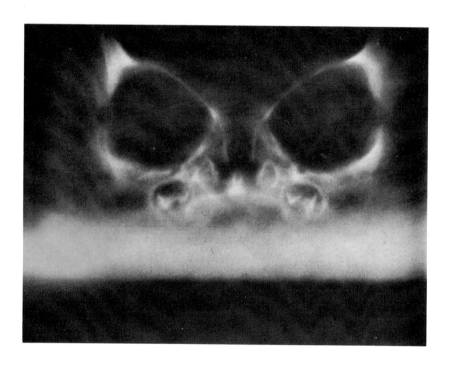

The calcified portion of each DECIDUAL MOLAR is conspicuous within the lucent chamber of its crypts. The portion of the MAXILLA between the nasal chamber and the orbit is essentially a shell about the antrum.

Each infraorbital canal, in the floor of the orbit, is a lucency surrounded by dense bone.

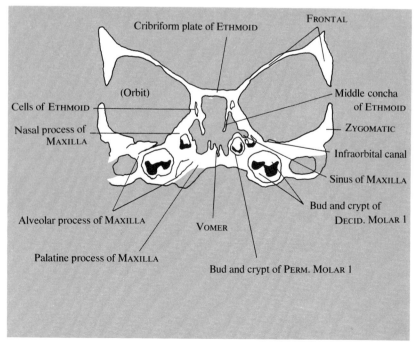

Figure 4.11

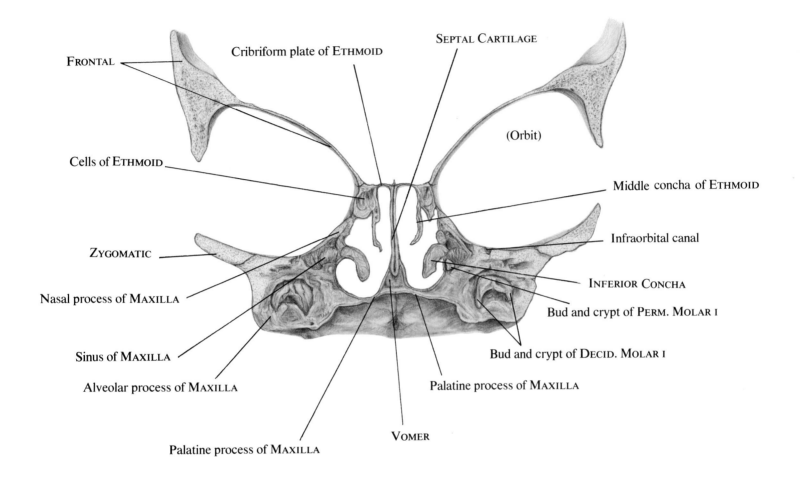

FRONTAL

Cribriform plate of ETHMOID

SEPTAL CARTILAGE

Cells of ETHMOID

(Orbit)

Middle concha of ETHMOID

ZYGOMATIC

Infraorbital canal

Nasal process of MAXILLA

INFERIOR CONCHA

Bud and crypt of PERM. MOLAR I

Sinus of MAXILLA

Bud and crypt of DECID. MOLAR I

Alveolar process of MAXILLA

Palatine process of MAXILLA

Palatine process of MAXILLA

VOMER

The MAXILLA is sectioned through its alveolar, palatine, orbital and nasal processes. The bud and crypt of DECIDUAL MOLAR 1 and the bud of PERMANENT MOLAR 1 are well shown. The palatine processes meet at a median suture; they are distinguished from the VOMER and from the ETH-MOID.

The INFERIOR CONCHA is clearly demarcated from the ETHMOID on the right. The ethmoidal cells are prominent superior and lateral to the nasal chamber, at the base of the middle concha. The antrum occupies much of the mass of the MAXILLA between the nasal chamber and the orbit; the meatus of the antrum into the nasal chamber is not shown.

Figure 4.12

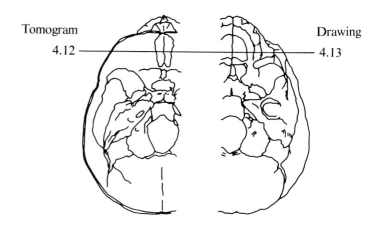

Tomogram
4.12 ——————— 4.13
Drawing

The bone between the nasal chamber and the orbit is essentially a delicate enclosure of the cells in the ETHMOID and the antrum in the MAXILLA.
In the palate and the adjacent medial wall of the MOLAR crypt, the bone is radiographically dense.
The lateral wall of the orbit is formed by masses of cancellous bone of the ZYGOMATIC and of the FRONTAL.

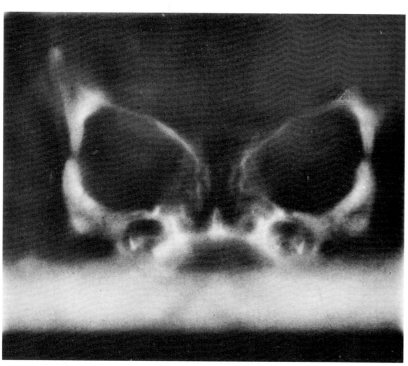

Superior concha of ETHMOID
Cribriform plate
FRONTAL
Sinus
Middle concha
ZYGOMATIC
INFERIOR CONCHA
VOMER
Infraorbital canal
Palatine process of MAXILLA
Bud and crypt of DECID. MOLAR 2

Figure 4.13

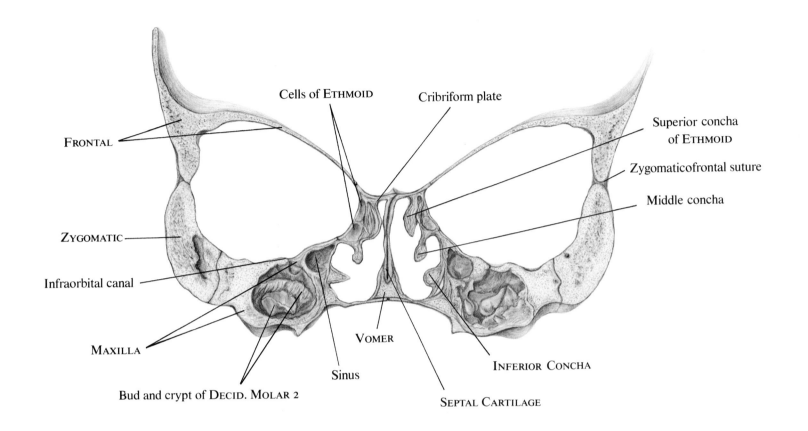

FRONTAL

Cells of ETHMOID

Cribriform plate

Superior concha of ETHMOID

Zygomaticofrontal suture

Middle concha

ZYGOMATIC

Infraorbital canal

MAXILLA

VOMER

Sinus

INFERIOR CONCHA

Bud and crypt of DECID. MOLAR 2

SEPTAL CARTILAGE

This section demonstrates the relation of the oral and orbital elements which is distinctive in the infant, compared with the human adult: the molar portion of the alvelar process constitutes the floor of the orbit. The infraorbital canal is a shallow indentation in that floor, and also is a part of the wall of the MOLAR 2 crypt.

The FRONTAL and ZYGOMATIC approximate at this level, completing enclosure of the orbit.

Figure 4.14

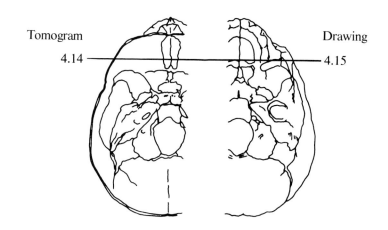

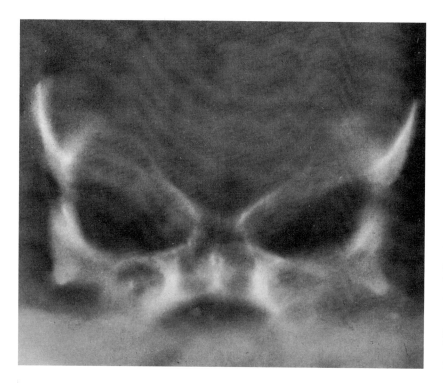

This radiographic section demonstrates the small vertical dimension of the nasal area compared with adult. The nose is also simpler, with smaller conchae and smaller ethmoidal cells. The paramendian plates of the VOMER extend about half of the vertical dimension of the septum.

The orbits are progressively narrower in medial direction. They are continuous with the temporal fossa.

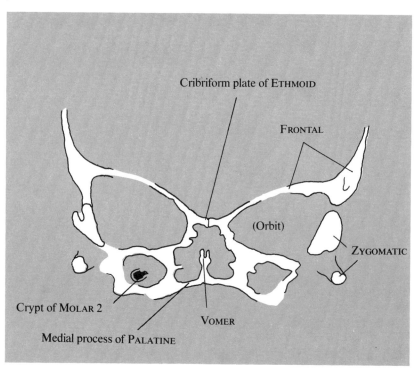

Cribriform plate of ETHMOID

FRONTAL

(Orbit)

ZYGOMATIC

Crypt of MOLAR 2

VOMER

Medial process of PALATINE

Figure 4.15

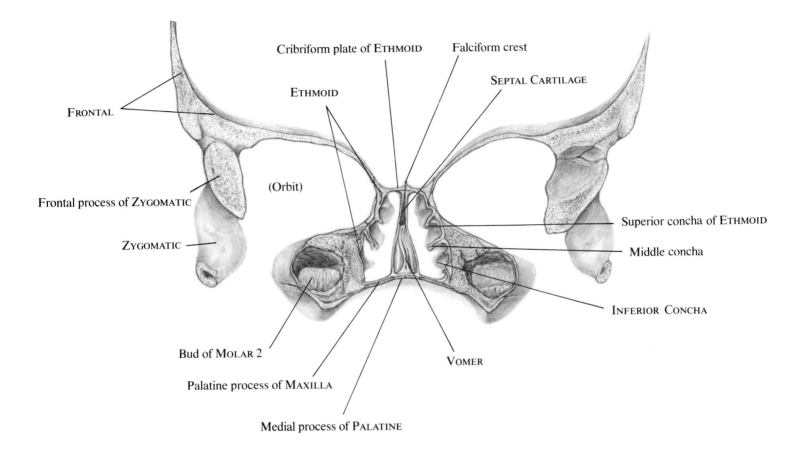

FRONTAL

Cribriform plate of ETHMOID

Falciform crest

ETHMOID

SEPTAL CARTILAGE

Frontal process of ZYGOMATIC

(Orbit)

Superior concha of ETHMOID

ZYGOMATIC

Middle concha

INFERIOR CONCHA

Bud of MOLAR 2

VOMER

Palatine process of MAXILLA

Medial process of PALATINE

This is the posterior portion of the MAXILLA. The bud and crypt of DECIDUAL MOLAR 2 are sectioned in their posterior portion. And the section passes through the suture between the palatal process corresponding medial of the MAXILLA and the PALATINE.

The VOMER is a pair of simple vertical planes. The ETHMOID lines the nasal chamber laterally and superiorly, with protruding conchae.

At this level, the roof of the orbit is superior to the cribiform plate.

Figure 4.16

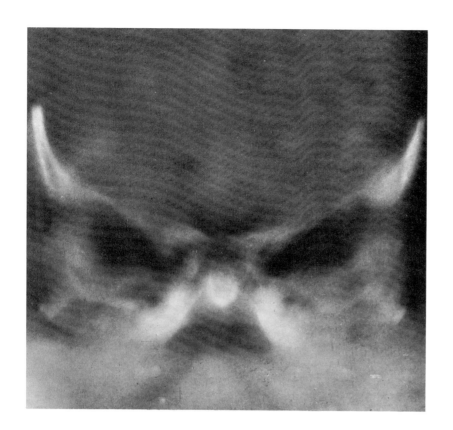

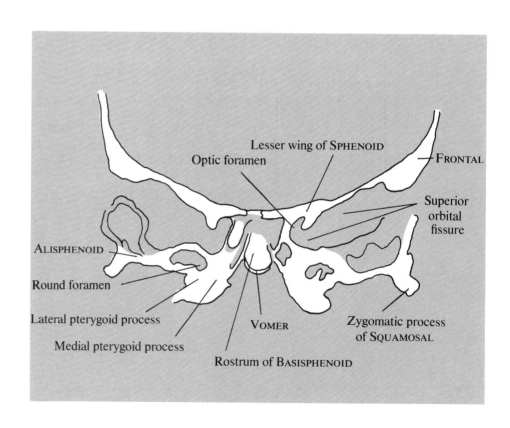

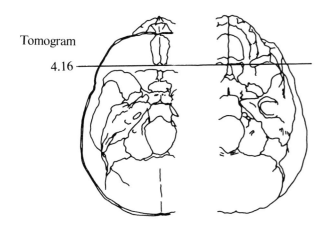

This section is through the posterior choanae, the posterior foramena of the orbit and the temporal fossa.

The optic foramen is more distinct on the right, where it is bounded by the roots of the lesser wing. The section is slightly anterior to the superior orbital fissure and the round foramen.

Figure 4.17 A-D

Supplementary coronal plane tomograms (A and C) and matching anatomical sections (B and D) from an additional specimen, a separate SPHENOID bone, which developmentally approximates the specimen of Chapter 4. Selected particularly for additional demonstration of orbitosphenoid area.

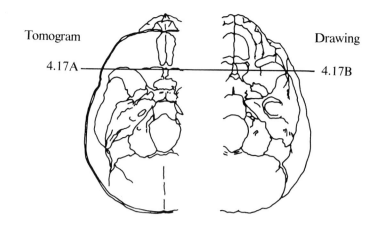

Tomogram   Drawing

4.17A ————————————— 4.17B

Figure 4.17 A

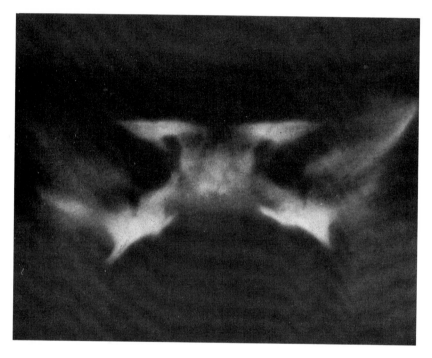

Tomogram through lesser wing and body of BASI-SPHENOID. Through greater wing and lateral pterygoid process of ALISPHENOID.
The optic canal is well defined by the anterior and posterior wings. Note the relative lucency of the inferior portion of the BASISPHENOID.
The lateral pterygoid process, of dense bone, is sharply outlined.

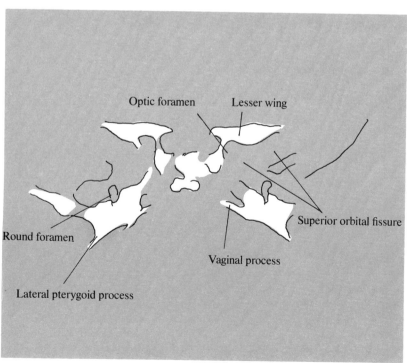

Optic foramen   Lesser wing

Round foramen

Lateral pterygoid process

Vaginal process

Superior orbital fissure

Figure 4.17 B

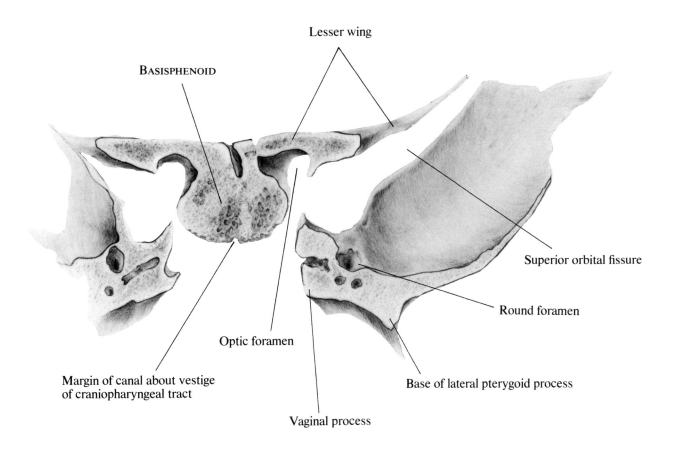

This section is through the optic foramen close to the sulcus of the optic chiasm, the superior orbital fissure and the round foramen.

The lesser wings, formed from symmetrical ossification centers, have not approximated in the midline. The inferior portion of the BASISPHENOID about the vestige of the craniopharyngeal tract, and extending toward the articulation with ALISPHE-NOID, was friable and disintegrated during the grinding of the specimen.

Figure 4.17 C

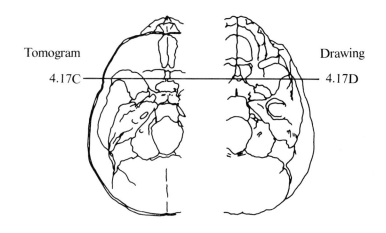

Tomogram   Drawing

4.17C —————————————————— 4.17D

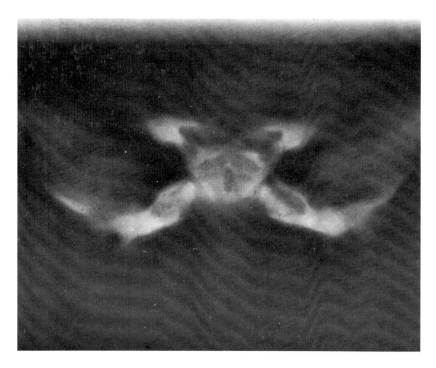

Tomogram is through the junction of the optic canals with the chiasmatic sulcus.

The canal about the vestige of the craniopharyngeal tract is distinctly outlined.

The articulation of the BASISPHENOID and ALISPHENOID is an irregular bony conglomeration.

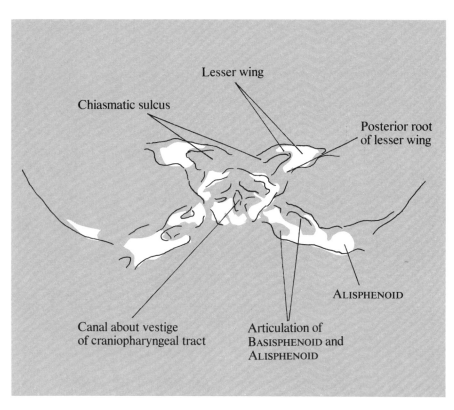

Chiasmatic sulcus

Lesser wing

Posterior root of lesser wing

ALISPHENOID

Canal about vestige of craniopharyngeal tract

Articulation of BASISPHENOID and ALISPHENOID

Figure 4.17 D

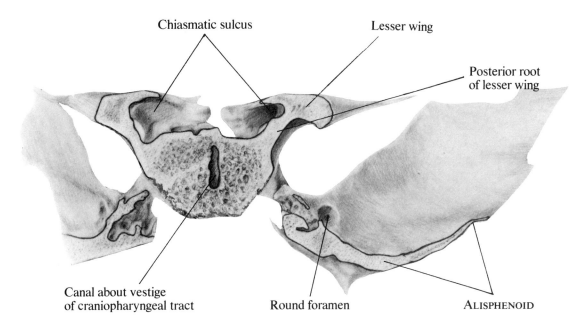

Chiasmatic sulcus   Lesser wing

Posterior root
of lesser wing

Canal about vestige
of craniopharyngeal tract

Round foramen   ALISPHENOID

Section through the chiasmatic sulcus and the posterior wing.
The friable inferior portion of BASISPHENOID of this section,
like that of 19B, disintegrated during the preparation.

Figure 4.18

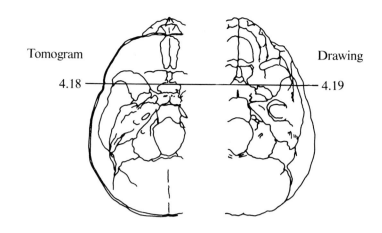

Tomogram   Drawing

4.18 ————————————— 4.19

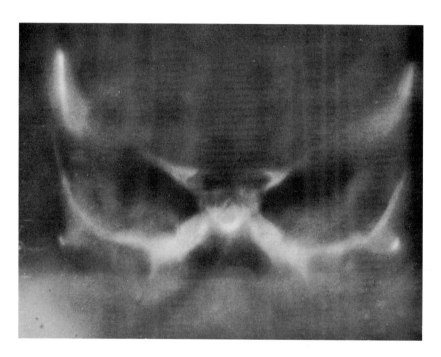

The **BASISPHENOID** is shaped radiographically as a broad rounded triangle. The central lucency of the canal about the vestige of the craniopharyngeal tract is in the form of an inverted V.

The radiographic contour of the **ALISPHENOID** corresponds closely with that in the corresponding anatomical section, including the site of the round foramen. The **PTERYGOID** is demarcated by suture from the medial pterygoid process.

The lateral portion of the lesser wing, at the side of the chiasmatic sulcus, is of dense bone.

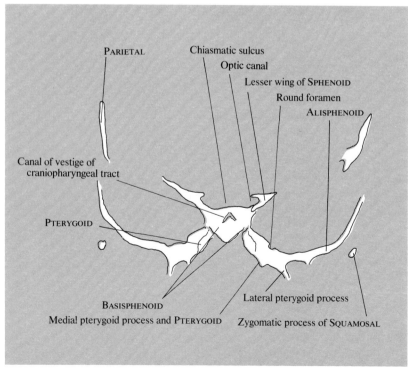

Figure 4.19

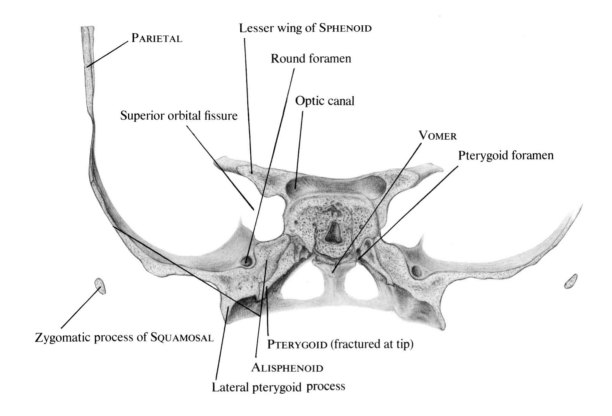

PARIETAL

Lesser wing of SPHENOID

Round foramen

Optic canal

Superior orbital fissure

VOMER

Pterygoid foramen

Zygomatic process of SQUAMOSAL

PTERYGOID (fractured at tip)

ALISPHENOID

Lateral pterygoid process

This section includes the BASISPHENOID, the ALISPHEN-OID, the PTERYGOID, and the lesser wing. The canal about the vestige of the craniopharyngeal tract (pouch of Rathke) is prominent in the center of the BASISPHENOID.

The ALISPHENOID is sectioned through its greatest mass. The expansion about the posterior orifice of the round foramen indents the bone in this plane. The "wing-like" thin plate extends lateralward as the superior wall of the temporal fossa. The lateral pterygoid process is short and blunted, in the infant. In the young infant, the PTERYGOID is a separate bone approximating the BASISPHENOID and ALISPHENOID and extending inferiorly as the hamulus (lost in this specimen, see Figure 3.3. The pterygoid foramen is located between the PTERYGOID and the lateral margin of the VOMER.

The sulcus of the optic chiasm is superior to tthe BASISPHEN-OID and enclosed laterally and anteriorly by the lesser wing. The optic foramen extends anterolaterally from it, between the anterior and posterior roots of the lesser wing.

Figure 4.20

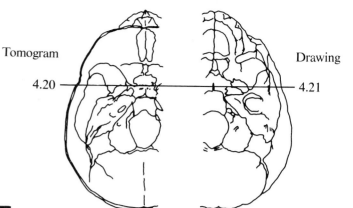

Tomogram   Drawing

4.20   4.21

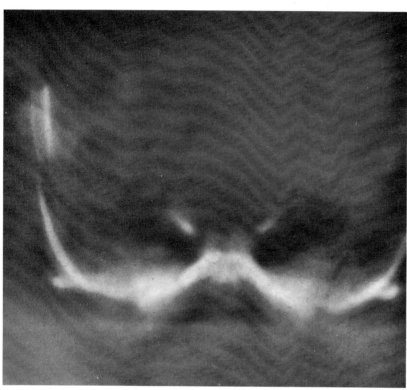

The **BASISPHENOID, ALISPHENOID** and lesser wing are essentially identical in arrangement and mass with the accompanying anatomical section, 4.21.

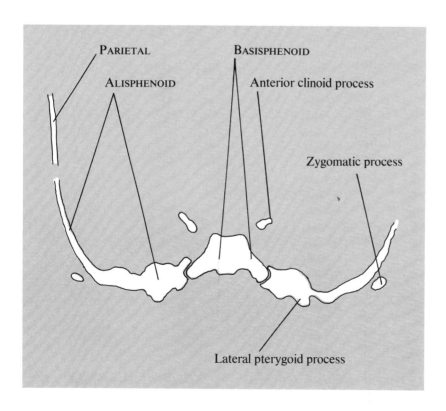

PARIETAL   BASISPHENOID

ALISPHENOID   Anterior clinoid process

Zygomatic process

Lateral pterygoid process

Figure 4.21

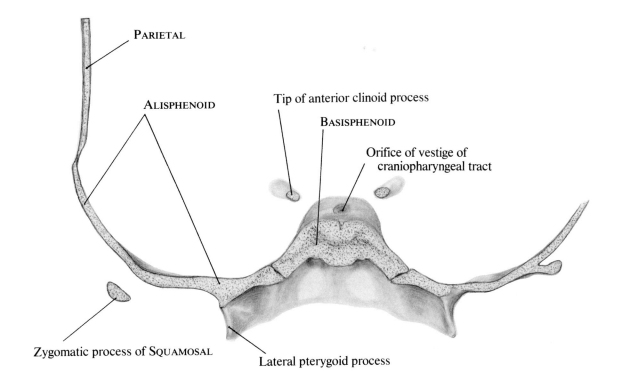

PARIETAL

ALISPHENOID

Tip of anterior clinoid process

BASISPHENOID

Orifice of vestige of
craniopharyngeal tract

Zygomatic process of SQUAMOSAL

Lateral pterygoid process

The ALISPHENOID and BASISPHENOID approximate at a simple suture.

The lesser wing is represented by the posterior tip of the anterior clinoid process.

This section is through the hypophyseal fossa and the roof of the epipharynx. The BASISPHENOID is saddle-shaped. The superior orifice of the canal about the vestige of the hypophyseal tract is immediately anterior to this section.

Figure 4.22

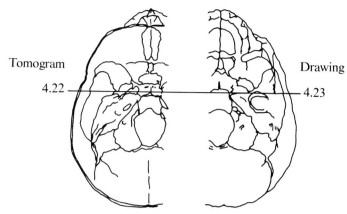

Tomogram   Drawing

4.22 ———— 4.23

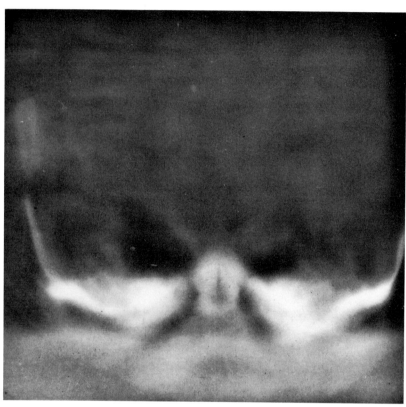

The median cleft in the BASISPHENOID is prominent.

The opacity of the ALISPHENOID is also larger than in the tomogram of Figure 4.20, reflecting the contour of the bone, which is oblique to the coronal plane.

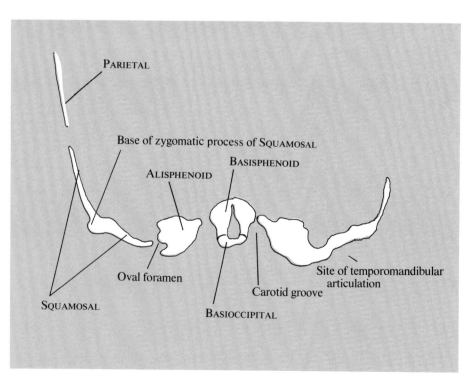

PARIETAL

Base of zygomatic process of SQUAMOSAL

ALISPHENOID

BASISPHENOID

Oval foramen

SQUAMOSAL

BASIOCCIPITAL

Carotid groove

Site of temporomandibular articulation

Figure 4.23

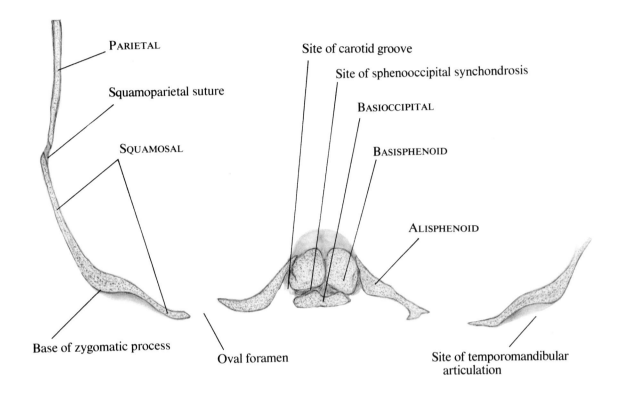

PARIETAL

Squamoparietal suture

SQUAMOSAL

Base of zygomatic process

Site of carotid groove

Site of sphenooccipital synchondrosis

BASIOCCIPITAL

BASISPHENOID

ALISPHENOID

Oval foramen

Site of temporomandibular articulation

This section is through thte approximation of the BASISPHEN-OID and BASIOCCIPITAL. The posterior end of the BASISPHENOID has a median cleft. The posterior mass, or dorsum sellae, of the hypophyseal fossa is entirely chondral in the young infant, and is missing from the skeletal specimen. Likewise, the mass of the sphenooccipital synchondrosis is diminished.

Only the anterior lip of the BASISPHENOID is shown.

The small plate of the ALISPHENOID joins the BASISPHE-NOID at a simple suture.

The SQUAMOSAL is sectioned at the base of the zygomatic process.

Figure 4.24*

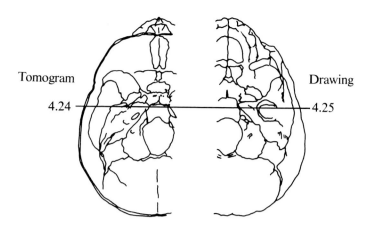

Tomogram ——— 4.24 ——— 4.25 ——— Drawing

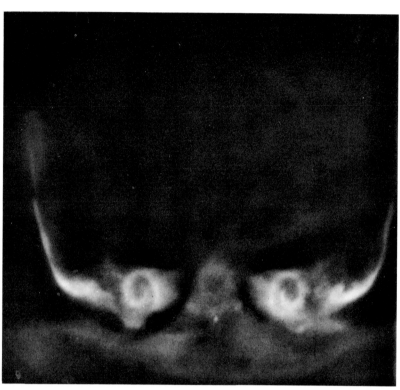

The MALLEUS and the lateral wall of the tympanic cavity are well shown in this tomogram. The tegmen is less distinct than in tomograms more posterior.

The lucency of the cochlea is sharply outlined by dense bone.

The petrooccipital suture, between the BASIOCCIPITAL and medial tip of the PETROSAL is well delineated.

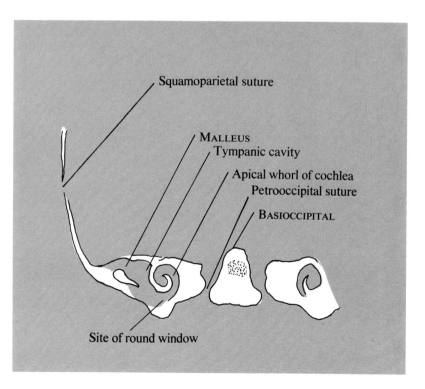

Squamoparietal suture

MALLEUS
Tympanic cavity

Apical whorl of cochlea
Petrooccipital suture

BASIOCCIPITAL

Site of round window

*The tomograms and the corresponding anatomic sections posterior to the plane of Figure 4.24 and 4.25 are each at approximately 1 mm. intervals.

Figure 4.25

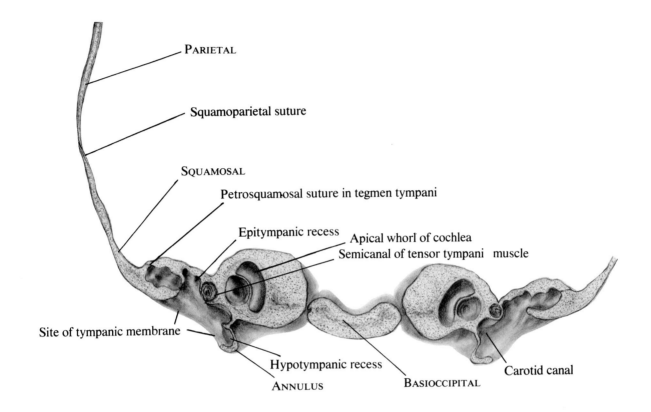

PARIETAL

Squamoparietal suture

SQUAMOSAL

Petrosquamosal suture in tegmen tympani

Epitympanic recess

Apical whorl of cochlea

Semicanal of tensor tympani muscle

Site of tympanic membrane

Hypotympanic recess

ANNULUS

BASIOCCIPITAL

Carotid canal

The cochlea is sectioned through the anterior portion of the tympanic cavity. The tegmen is thick and the epitympanic recess irregularly indents it. The tensor tympani muscle is well shown within its semicanal.

The section is also through the anterior margin of the basal and apical whorls of the cochlea.

Figure 4.26

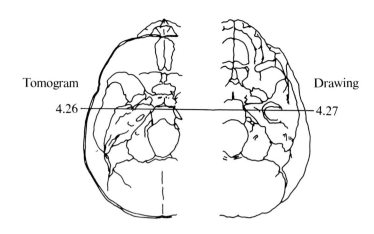

Tomogram   Drawing

4.26 —————— 4.27

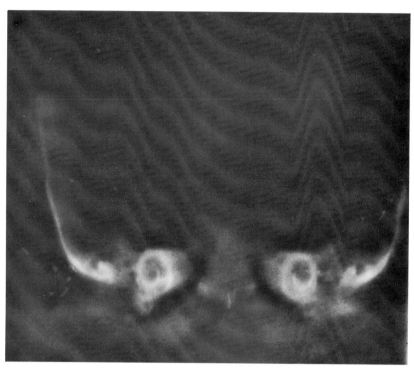

The tegmen of the tympanic cavity is not distinguishable in this tomogram.

The basal and apical whorls of the cochlea are sharply outlined.

The flat BASIOCCIPITAL is oriented obliquely to the coronal plane and, hence, is differently demonstrated in the anatomical and radiographic sections.

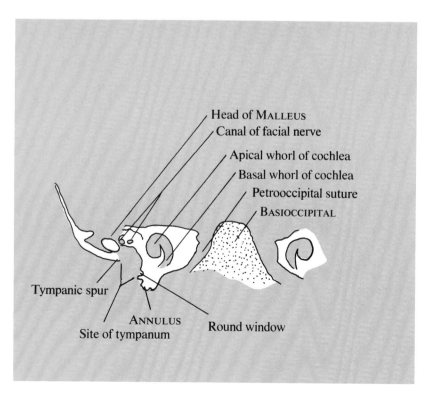

Head of MALLEUS
Canal of facial nerve
Apical whorl of cochlea
Basal whorl of cochlea
Petrooccipital suture
BASIOCCIPITAL
Tympanic spur
ANNULUS
Site of tympanum
Round window

Figure 4.27

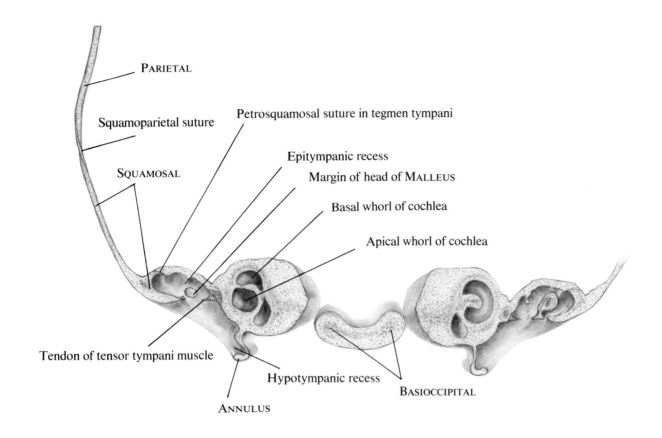

PARIETAL

Squamoparietal suture

Petrosquamosal suture in tegmen tympani

SQUAMOSAL

Epitympanic recess

Margin of head of MALLEUS

Basal whorl of cochlea

Apical whorl of cochlea

Tendon of tensor tympani muscle

Hypotympanic recess

BASIOCCIPITAL

ANNULUS

The ANNULUS is sectioned in its inferior portion. The MAL-LEUS is sectioned through its head. The tendon of the tensor tympani muscle is shown on each side. The tegmen of the tympanic cavity is thin.

The apical whorl is sectioned close to the cupula. The canal of the facial nerve is shown at its hiatus at the site of the geniculate ganglion.

Figure 4.28

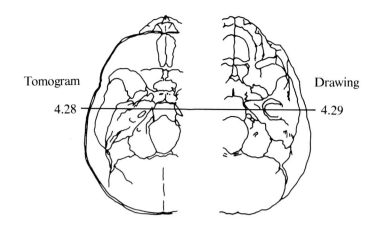

Tomogram
4.28 ——————————————— 4.29
Drawing

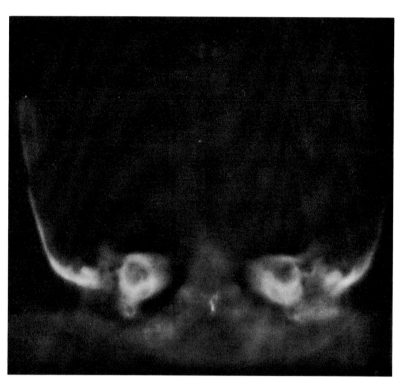

The lateral wall of the tympanic cavity and the posterior portion of the MALLEUS are distinct. The hiatus of the facial canal is shown on the right. Two adjacent parts of the canal, adjacent to the hiatus, are shown on the left.

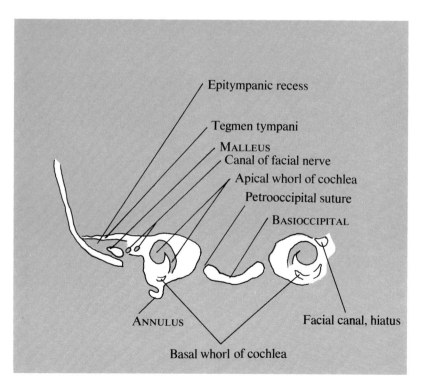

Epitympanic recess

Tegmen tympani

MALLEUS
Canal of facial nerve
Apical whorl of cochlea
Petrooccipital suture

BASIOCCIPITAL

ANNULUS

Facial canal, hiatus

Basal whorl of cochlea

Figure 4.29

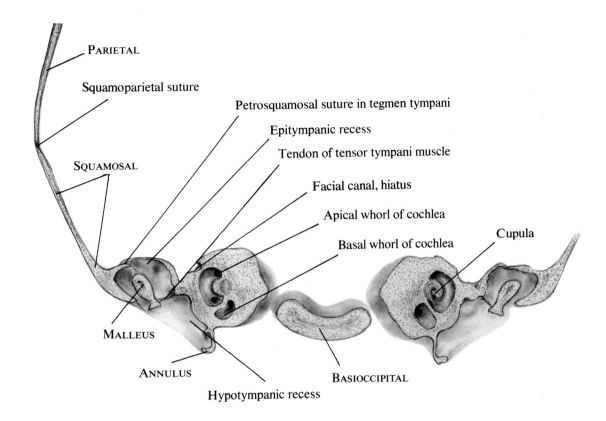

PARIETAL

Squamoparietal suture

Petrosquamosal suture in tegmen tympani

Epitympanic recess

Tendon of tensor tympani muscle

SQUAMOSAL

Facial canal, hiatus

Apical whorl of cochlea

Cupula

Basal whorl of cochlea

MALLEUS

ANNULUS

BASIOCCIPITAL

Hypotympanic recess

The MALLEUS is sectioned through its posterior portion.
The medial portion of the canal of the facial nerve lies superior
to the cochlea. The lateral portion is in the wall of the tympanic
cavity.
The apical whorl of the cochlea is separated from the internal
acoustic meatus by the thin cribriform lamina. The basal whorl
is sectioned through its posterior margin.

Figure 4.30

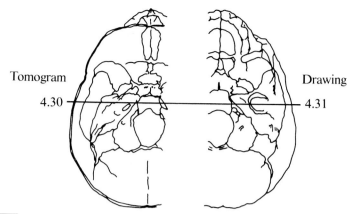

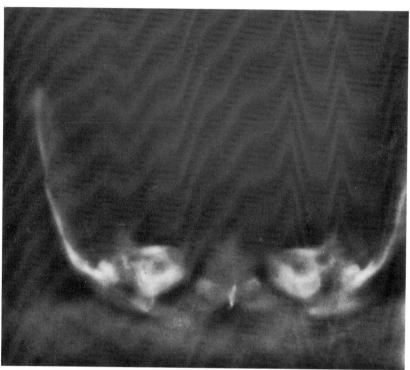

The opacity of the bodies of the INCUS and MAL-LEUS are fused in this tomogram.

The lucency of the meatus is combined with that of the apical whorl. The lucency of the anterior semi-circular canal is also evident.

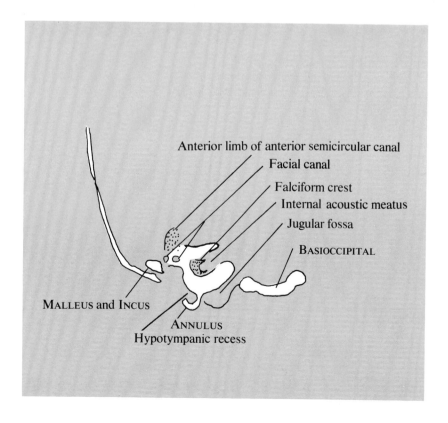

Anterior limb of anterior semicircular canal
Facial canal
Falciform crest
Internal acoustic meatus
Jugular fossa
BASIOCCIPITAL
MALLEUS and INCUS
ANNULUS
Hypotympanic recess

Figure 4.31

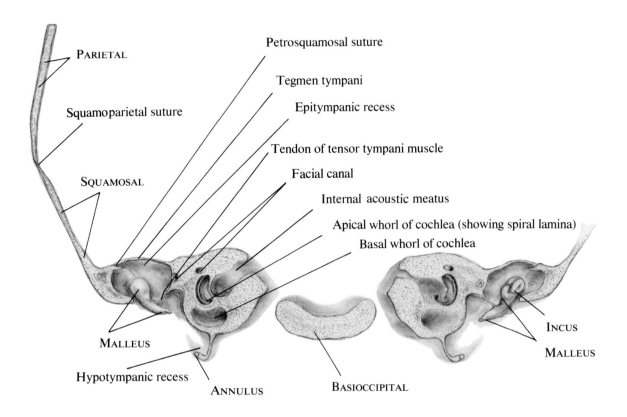

PARIETAL

Squamoparietal suture

SQUAMOSAL

MALLEUS

Hypotympanic recess

ANNULUS

Petrosquamosal suture

Tegmen tympani

Epitympanic recess

Tendon of tensor tympani muscle

Facial canal

Internal acoustic meatus

Apical whorl of cochlea (showing spiral lamina)

Basal whorl of cochlea

BASIOCCIPITAL

INCUS

MALLEUS

The INCUS and the neck of the MALLEUS are in this anatomical section.

The basal whorl of the cochlea indents the tympanic cavity as the promontory. The medial portion of the facial canal joins the internal acoustic meatus above the falciform crest. The lateral portion of this canal indents the tympanic cavity.

Figure 4.32

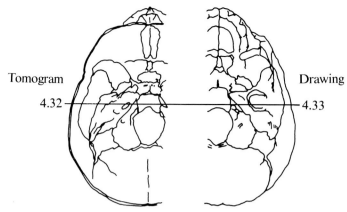

Tomogram   Drawing
4.32 ———————————————————— 4.33

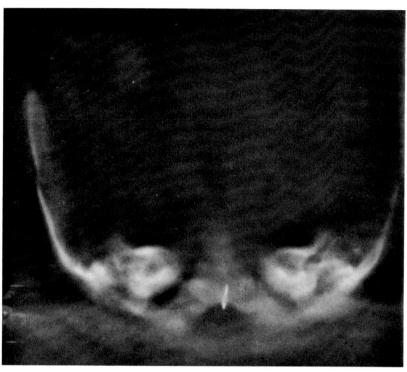

The bodies of the MALLEUS and INCUS are a common opacity in the tympanic cavity.

The lateral portion of the facial canal is visible in the margin of the tympanic cavity, inferior to the lateral semicircular canal. The anterior semicircular canal is seen indistinctly.

The internal acoustic meatus is fully demarcated. The jugular fossa is bulbous in contour.

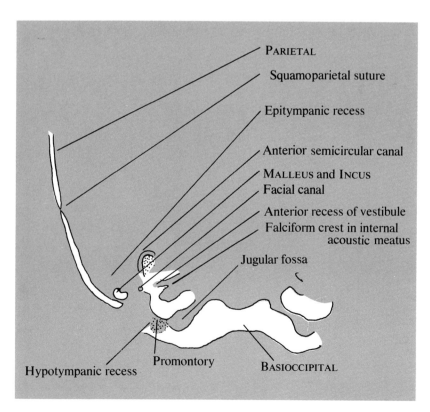

PARIETAL

Squamoparietal suture

Epitympanic recess

Anterior semicircular canal

MALLEUS and INCUS
Facial canal

Anterior recess of vestibule
Falciform crest in internal
                  acoustic meatus

Jugular fossa

Hypotympanic recess   Promontory   BASIOCCIPITAL

Figure 4.33

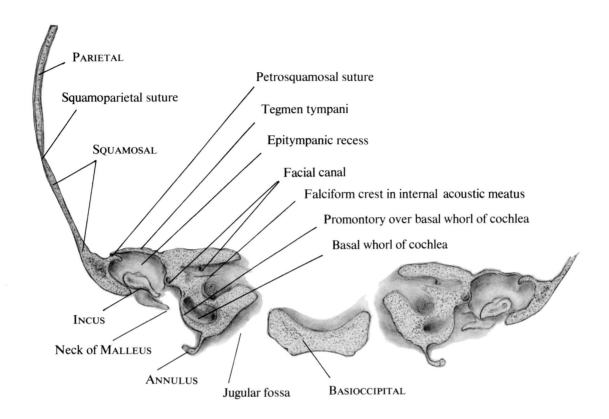

PARIETAL

Squamoparietal suture

SQUAMOSAL

Petrosquamosal suture

Tegmen tympani

Epitympanic recess

Facial canal

Falciform crest in internal acoustic meatus

Promontory over basal whorl of cochlea

Basal whorl of cochlea

INCUS

Neck of MALLEUS

ANNULUS

Jugular fossa

BASIOCCIPITAL

The INCUS is shown in most of its length. The body of MAL-
LEUS is in perspective; its neck is in the section.
The facial canal indents the medial wall of the tympanic cavity.
The falciform crest is at its greatest prominence in the internal
acoustic meatus.

Figure 4.34

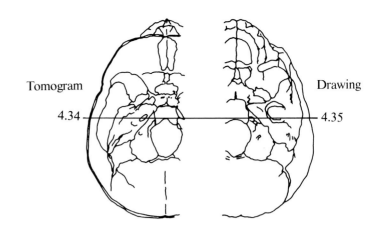

Tomogram   Drawing

4.34 ———————————— 4.35

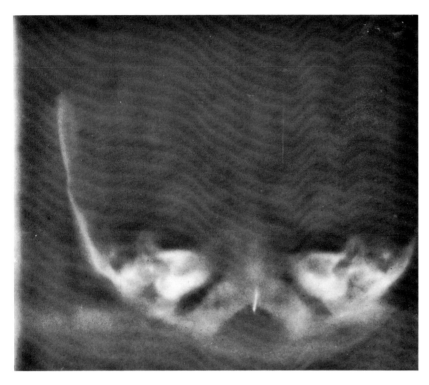

In this tomogram, the INCUS and the head of the STAPES are outlined in continuity.

The lucency of the basal whorl overlies that of the vestibule. The anterior limb of the anterior semi-circular canal is distinguishable in the arcuate eminence.

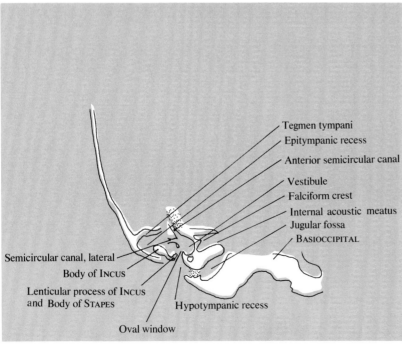

Tegmen tympani
Epitympanic recess
Anterior semicircular canal
Vestibule
Falciform crest
Internal acoustic meatus
Jugular fossa
BASIOCCIPITAL
Semicircular canal, lateral
Body of INCUS
Lenticular process of INCUS and Body of STAPES
Hypotympanic recess
Oval window

Figure 4.35

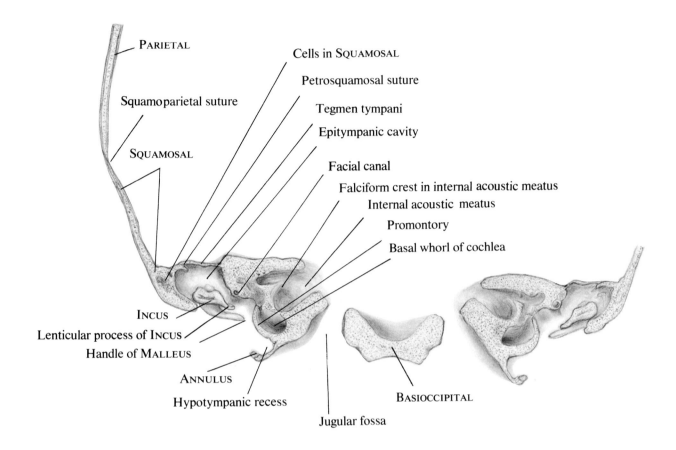

PARIETAL

Squamoparietal suture

SQUAMOSAL

Cells in SQUAMOSAL

Petrosquamosal suture

Tegmen tympani

Epitympanic cavity

Facial canal

Falciform crest in internal acoustic meatus

Internal acoustic meatus

Promontory

Basal whorl of cochlea

INCUS

Lenticular process of INCUS

Handle of MALLEUS

ANNULUS

Hypotympanic recess

Jugular fossa

BASIOCCIPITAL

This anatomical section is through the INCUS and the handle of the MALLEUS.

The tympanic cavity is extended laterally into the SQUAMO-SAL by small air cells. The tegmen is thin.

The portion of the internal acoustic meatus inferior to the falciform crest closely approximates the basal whorl of the cochlea. The promontory over the basal whorl and the ridge over the facial canal demarcate the indentation of the tympanic cavity toward the oval window.

Figure 4.36

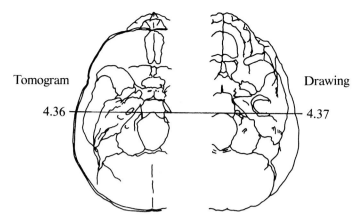

Tomogram   Drawing

4.36 —   — 4.37

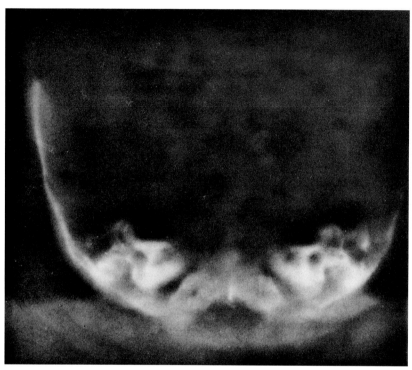

In this tomogram, the body of INCUS is shown. In the PETROSAL, there is continuity of the lucencies of the vestibule and of the posterior, lateral and anterior semicircular canals. The anterior canal is outlined by a portion of the arcuate eminence. The internal acoustic meatus is also well outlined.

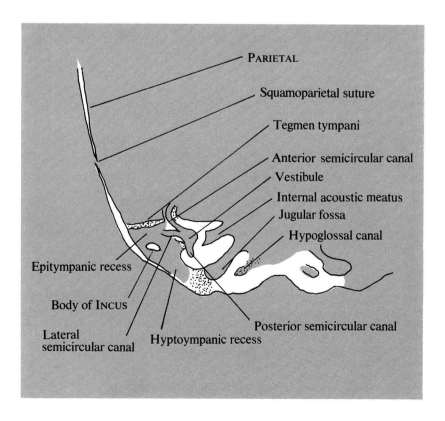

PARIETAL

Squamoparietal suture

Tegmen tympani

Anterior semicircular canal

Vestibule

Internal acoustic meatus

Jugular fossa

Hypoglossal canal

Epitympanic recess

Body of INCUS

Lateral semicircular canal

Hyptoympanic recess

Posterior semicircular canal

Figure 4.37

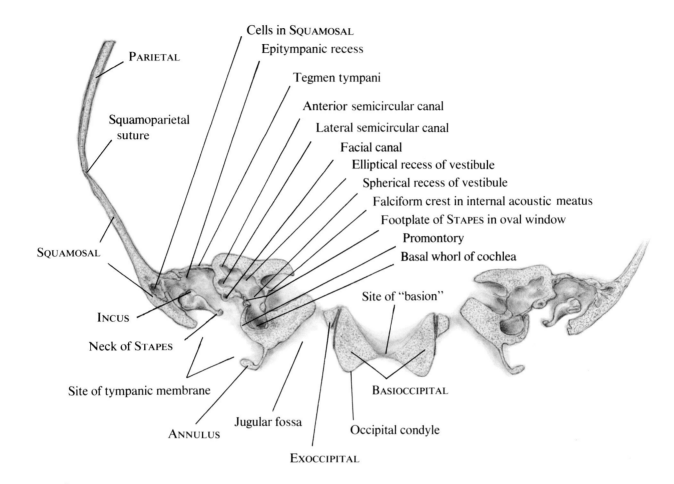

PARIETAL

Squamoparietal suture

SQUAMOSAL

INCUS

Neck of STAPES

Site of tympanic membrane

ANNULUS

Jugular fossa

EXOCCIPITAL

Cells in SQUAMOSAL

Epitympanic recess

Tegmen tympani

Anterior semicircular canal

Lateral semicircular canal

Facial canal

Elliptical recess of vestibule

Spherical recess of vestibule

Falciform crest in internal acoustic meatus

Footplate of STAPES in oval window

Promontory

Basal whorl of cochlea

Site of "basion"

BASIOCCIPITAL

Occipital condyle

This section includes the INCUS and the neck of the STAPES. In the anatomical section, the thin partition between the internal acoustic meatus and the basal whorl is perforated. The oval window, containing the footplate of the STAPES, is at the junction of the basal whorl and the spherical recess of the vestibule. The lateral and anterior semicircular canals extend from the elliptical recess. The lateral portion of the facial canal is seen in the wall of the tympanic cavity.

Figure 4.38

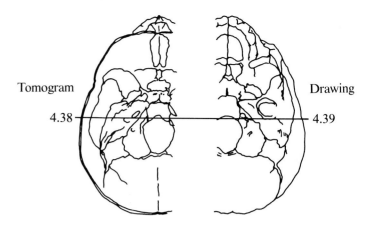

Tomogram   Drawing

4.38   4.39

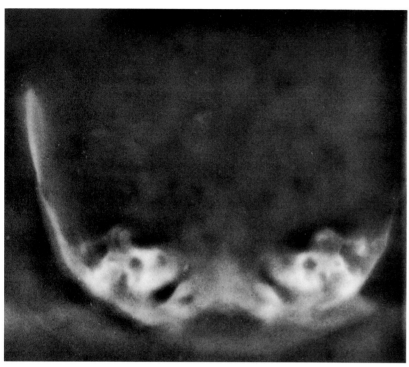

The INCUS and STAPES are shown in continuity. The internal acoustic meatus is shallow. A greater extent of the lateral and anterior semicircular canal is shown than in the tomogram of Figure 4.37. The subarcuate fossa is discernable in the anterior face of the PETROSAL, as an indentation toward the superior semicircular canal.

The hypoglossal canal is well shown in the EXOC-CIPITAL.

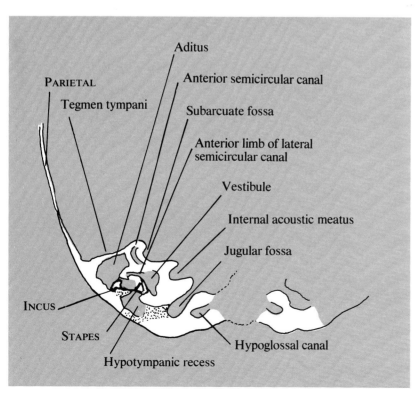

Figure 4.41

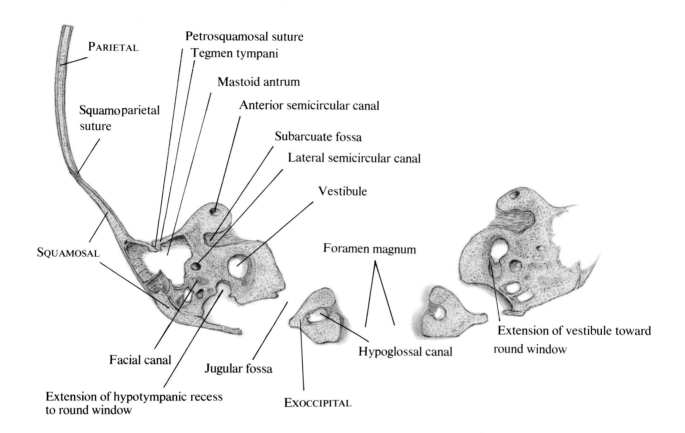

PARIETAL

Petrosquamosal suture

Tegmen tympani

Mastoid antrum

Anterior semicircular canal

Squamoparietal suture

Subarcuate fossa

Lateral semicircular canal

Vestibule

Foramen magnum

Extension of vestibule toward round window

SQUAMOSAL

Facial canal

Hypoglossal canal

Jugular fossa

Extension of hypotympanic recess to round window

EXOCCIPITAL

The vestibule is now an isolated ovoid cavity. Extension of the vestibule toward the round window is shown on the right. The lateral portion of the lateral semicircular canal indents the tympanic cavity. The superior portion of the anterior semicircular canal is within the arcuate eminence.

On the left, the hypotympanic recess extends toward the round window. The recess also approximates the jugular fossa.

The hypoglossal canal is seen in the EXOCCIPITAL.

Figure 4.42

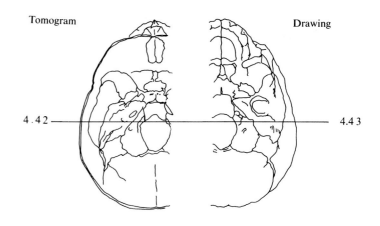

4.42 ———————————————————— 4.43

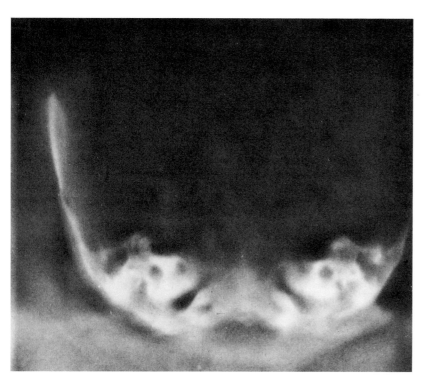

Within the **PETROSAL**, the vestibule, the internal acoustic meatus, and the subarcuate fossa are distinguished. The lateral semicircular canal approximates the lucency of the tympanic cavity. The anterior semicircular canal is enclosed by the superior margin of the arcuate eminence.

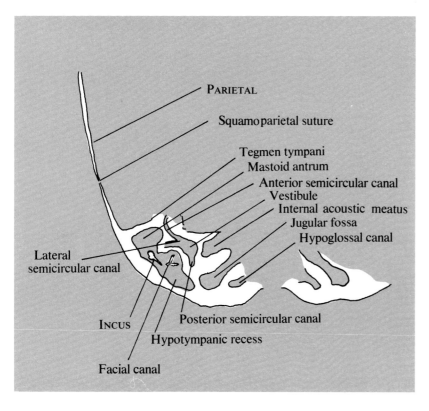

PARIETAL

Squamoparietal suture

Tegmen tympani
Mastoid antrum
Anterior semicircular canal
Vestibule
Internal acoustic meatus
Jugular fossa
Hypoglossal canal

Lateral
semicircular canal

INCUS

Posterior semicircular canal

Hypotympanic recess

Facial canal

Figure 4.43

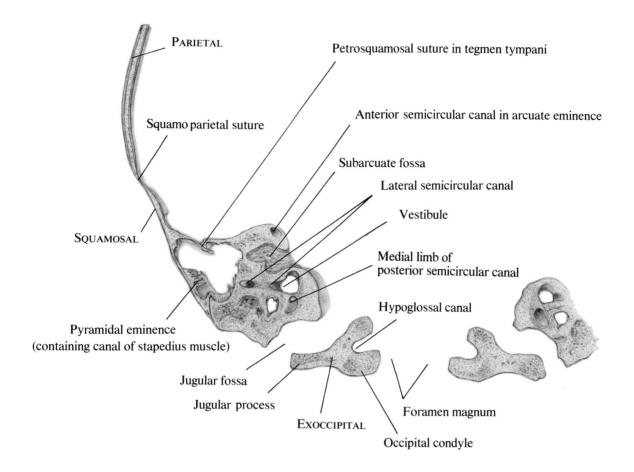

PARIETAL

Petrosquamosal suture in tegmen tympani

Squamo parietal suture

Anterior semicircular canal in arcuate eminence

Subarcuate fossa

Lateral semicircular canal

Vestibule

SQUAMOSAL

Medial limb of
posterior semicircular canal

Hypoglossal canal

Pyramidal eminence
(containing canal of stapedius muscle)

Jugular fossa

Jugular process

EXOCCIPITAL

Foramen magnum

Occipital condyle

In this anatomical section, the posterior limb of the lateral semicircular canal and the medial limb of the posterior semicircular canal join the vestibule. The anterior semicircular canal is in the posterior portion of the arcuate eminence about the subarcuate fossa.

The pyramidal eminence contains the canal of the stapedius muscle.

The EXOCCIPITAL contains the hypoglossal canal. It is extended lateralward as the jugular process.

Figure 4.44

 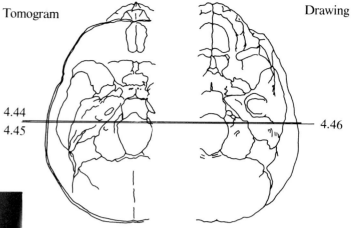

4.44
4.45
4.46

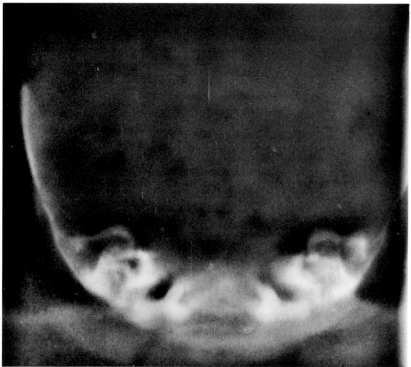

In this tomogram, the lateral and the anterior semi-circular canals are shown in continuity with the vestibule. And the subarcuate fossa is in continuity with the mastoid antrum.

The hypotympanic recess is shown in the tomogram but not in the anatomical section.

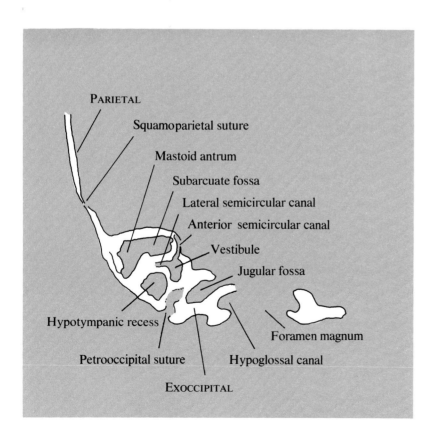

PARIETAL
Squamoparietal suture
Mastoid antrum
Subarcuate fossa
Lateral semicircular canal
Anterior semicircular canal
Vestibule
Jugular fossa
Hypotympanic recess
Foramen magnum
Petrooccipital suture
Hypoglossal canal
EXOCCIPITAL

Figure 4.46

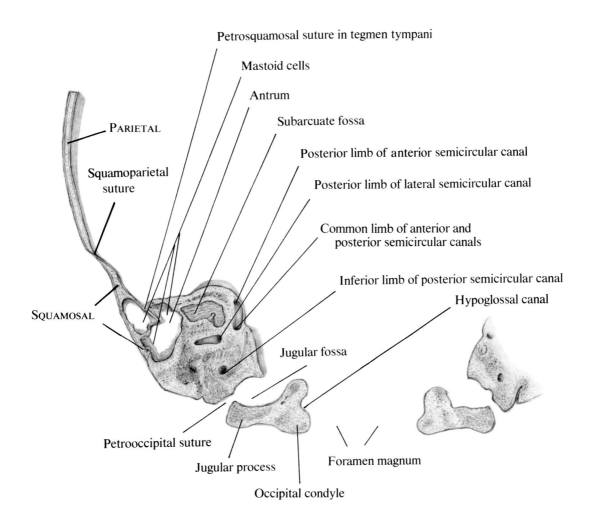

Petrosquamosal suture in tegmen tympani

Mastoid cells

Antrum

Subarcuate fossa

PARIETAL

Posterior limb of anterior semicircular canal

Squamoparietal
suture

Posterior limb of lateral semicircular canal

Common limb of anterior and
posterior semicircular canals

Inferior limb of posterior semicircular canal

Hypoglossal canal

SQUAMOSAL

Jugular fossa

Petrooccipital suture

Jugular process

Foramen magnum

Occipital condyle

This anatomical section demonstrates the relation of the three semicircular canals immediately posterior to the vestibule. The lateral canal is sectioned through its posterior portion. The posterior canal is shown at its common crus with the anterior canal. The posterior portion of the subarcuate fossa extends nearly to the mastoid antrum.

The hypoglossal canal is a shallow indentation on the medial aspect of the EXOCCIPITAL. The jugular process approximates the PETROSAL at the petrooccipital suture.

Figure 4.45

Tomogram   Drawing

4.44
4.45   4.46

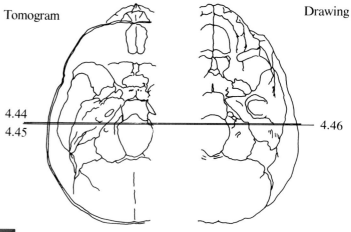

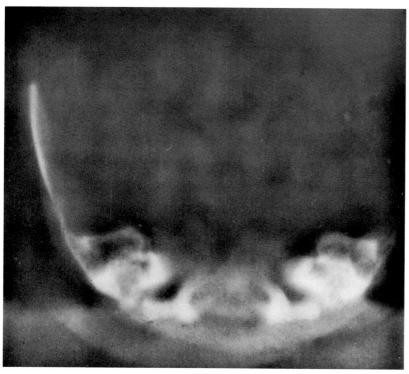

The anterior and the lateral semicircular canals are in continuity with the vestibule. The lucency of the subarcuate fossa is in continuity with that of the mastoid antrum. The hypotympanic recess is incompletely distinguishable.

The PETROSAL now approximates the jugular process of the EXOCCIPITAL, at the petrosquamosal suture. The hypoglossal canal is a shallow indentation in the EXOCCIPITAL.

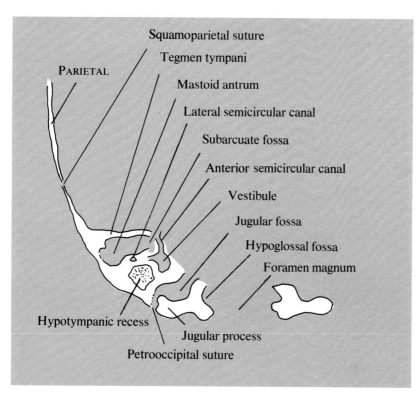

Squamoparietal suture
Tegmen tympani
PARIETAL
Mastoid antrum
Lateral semicircular canal
Subarcuate fossa
Anterior semicircular canal
Vestibule
Jugular fossa
Hypoglossal fossa
Foramen magnum
Hypotympanic recess
Jugular process
Petrooccipital suture

Figure 4.46

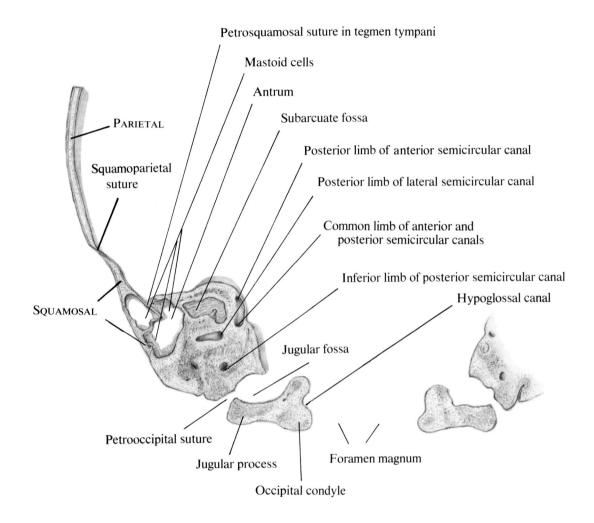

Petrosquamosal suture in tegmen tympani

Mastoid cells

Antrum

Subarcuate fossa

Posterior limb of anterior semicircular canal

Posterior limb of lateral semicircular canal

Common limb of anterior and posterior semicircular canals

Inferior limb of posterior semicircular canal

Hypoglossal canal

PARIETAL

Squamoparietal suture

SQUAMOSAL

Jugular fossa

Petrooccipital suture

Jugular process

Foramen magnum

Occipital condyle

See legend on page 61.

Figure 4.47

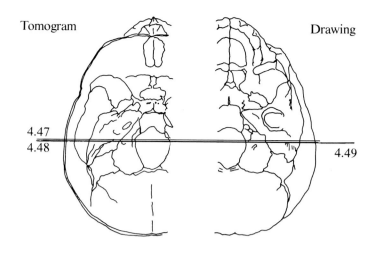

4.47
4.48

4.49

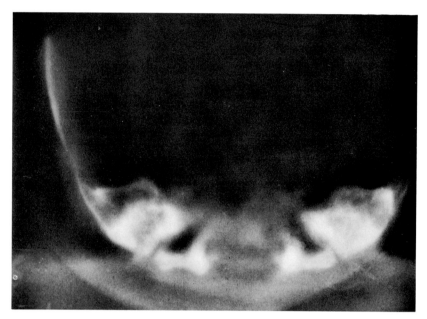

The vestibule and the hypotympanic recess are evident in the tomogram, though not in the corresponding anatomical section.

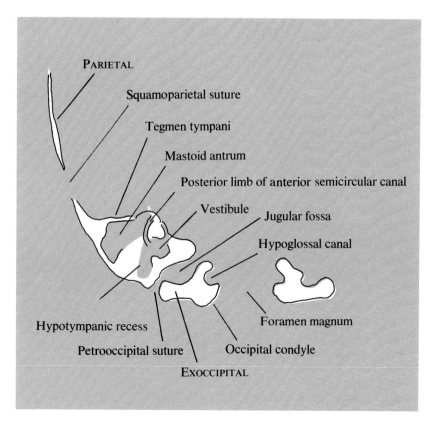

PARIETAL

Squamoparietal suture

Tegmen tympani

Mastoid antrum

Posterior limb of anterior semicircular canal

Vestibule

Jugular fossa

Hypoglossal canal

Hypotympanic recess

Petrooccipital suture

EXOCCIPITAL

Occipital condyle

Foramen magnum

Figure 4.49

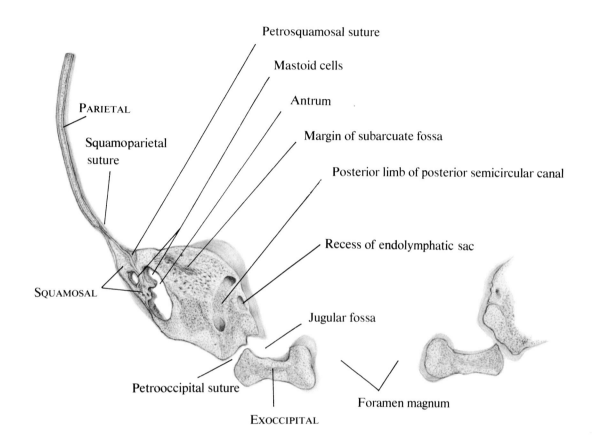

Petrosquamosal suture

Mastoid cells

Antrum

Margin of subarcuate fossa

Posterior limb of posterior semicircular canal

PARIETAL

Squamoparietal suture

Recess of endolymphatic sac

SQUAMOSAL

Jugular fossa

Petrooccipital suture

Foramen magnum

EXOCCIPITAL

The only element of the labyrinth shown in this anatomical section is the posterior limb of the posterior semicircular canal. The recess of the endolymphatic sac is medial to the curve of this canal. The aqueduct of the vestibule is not visualized on these sections due to its obliquity to the coronal plane and its very narrow contour. The vestibule is slightly evident in the tomogram.

The tympanic cavity is represented only by the mastoid antrum and cells. The tegmen is a thick shelf of bone.

Figure 4.48

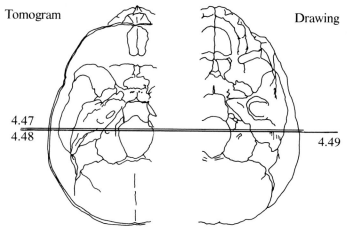

Tomogram   Drawing

4.47
4.48

4.49

The posterior limb of the posterior semicircular canal and the recess of the endolymphatic sac are outlined by dense bone. But most of the lateral portion of the **PETROSAL** is cancellous. Accordingly, the margins of the antrum and of the subarcuate mossa are not well distinguished in this area.

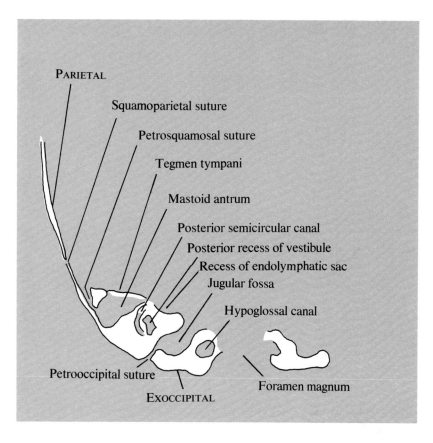

PARIETAL

Squamoparietal suture

Petrosquamosal suture

Tegmen tympani

Mastoid antrum

Posterior semicircular canal

Posterior recess of vestibule

Recess of endolymphatic sac

Jugular fossa

Hypoglossal canal

Petrooccipital suture

EXOCCIPITAL

Foramen magnum

Figure 4.49

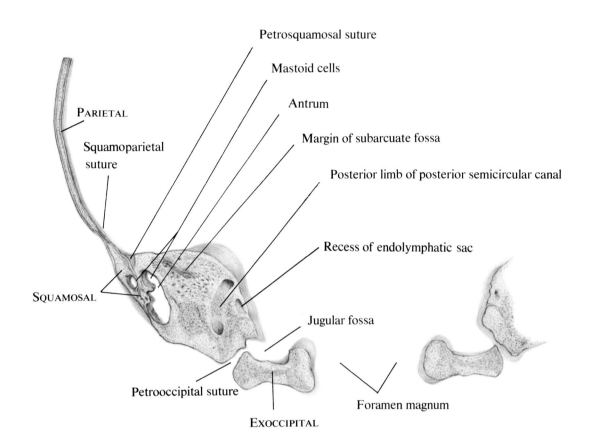

Petrosquamosal suture

Mastoid cells

Antrum

Margin of subarcuate fossa

Posterior limb of posterior semicircular canal

Recess of endolymphatic sac

PARIETAL

Squamoparietal suture

SQUAMOSAL

Jugular fossa

Petrooccipital suture

Foramen magnum

EXOCCIPITAL

See legend in page 65.

Figure 4.50

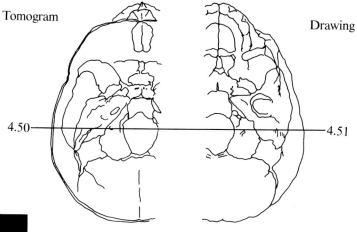

Tomogram   Drawing

4.50 ————————————————— 4.51

The tomogram corresponds closely to the anatomical section fo Figure 4.51.

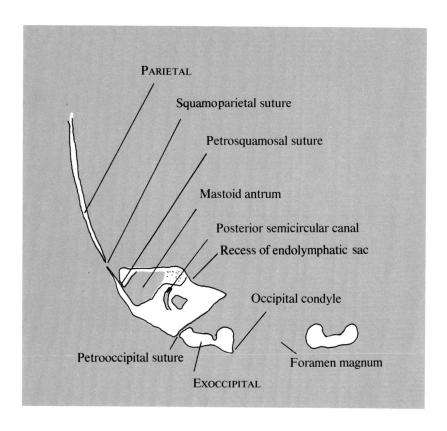

PARIETAL

Squamoparietal suture

Petrosquamosal suture

Mastoid antrum

Posterior semicircular canal

Recess of endolymphatic sac

Occipital condyle

Petrooccipital suture

Foramen magnum

EXOCCIPITAL

Figure 4.51

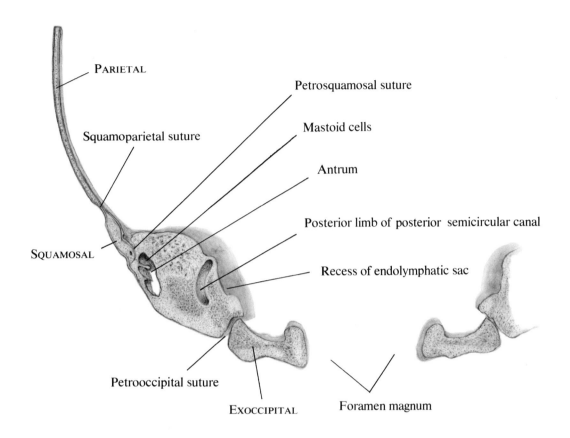

PARIETAL

Petrosquamosal suture

Squamoparietal suture

Mastoid cells

Antrum

Posterior limb of posterior semicircular canal

SQUAMOSAL

Recess of endolymphatic sac

Petrooccipital suture

EXOCCIPITAL

Foramen magnum

The **PETROSAL** is a bony mass except for the posterior margin of the posterior semicircular canal and the posterior end of the mastoid antrum. The recess of the endolympathic sac is shallow. The portion of the bone superior and medial to the mastoid antrum is loosely cancellous.

The **SQUAMOSAL** is a vertically short projection between the **PETROSAL** and the **PARIETAL**.

CHAPTER 5

Transverse Tomograms and Drawn Sections

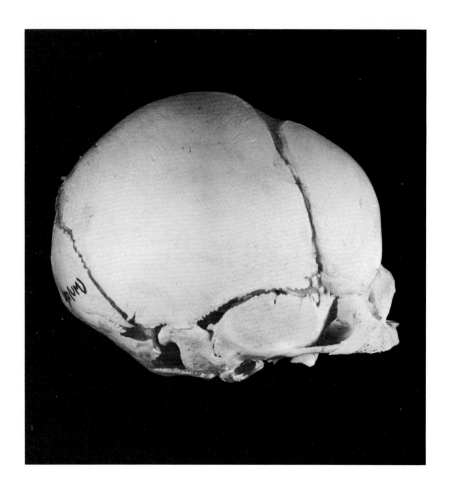

Figure 5.1
Photograph of specimen, lateral view

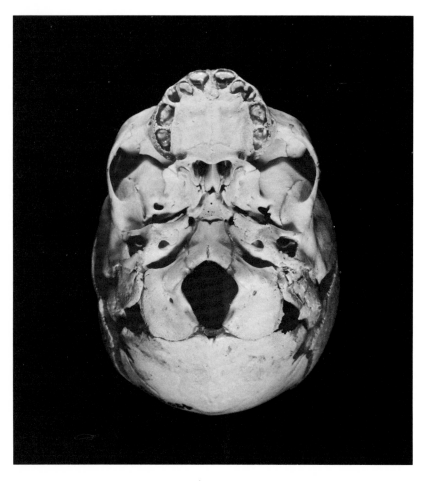

Figure 5.3
Photograph of specimen, inferior view

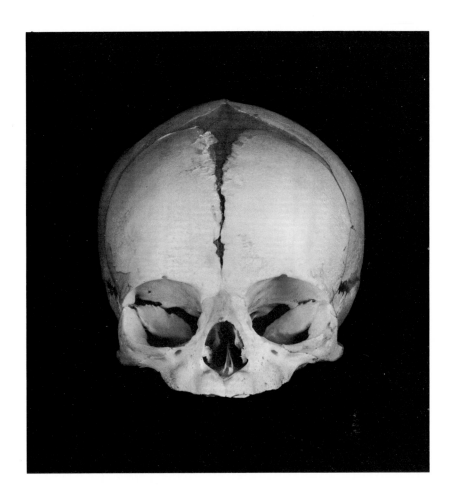

Figure 5.2
Photograph of specimen, frontal view

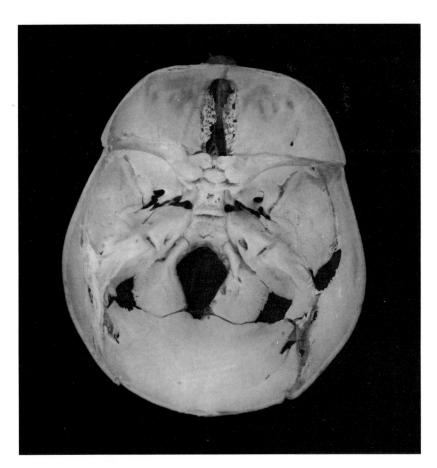

Figure 5.4
Photograph of specimen, superior view, roof of calvarium removed

Figure 5.5 Orientation of tomograms and drawings on paramedian schematic of cranium

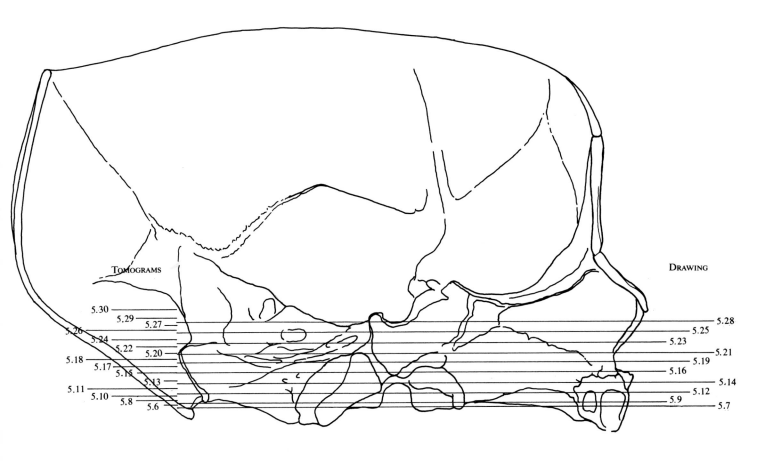

Figure 5.6

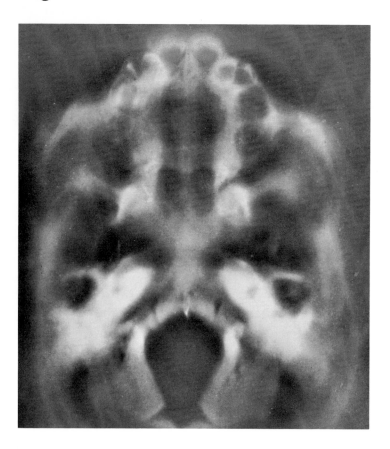

This tomogram corresponds with the drawing of Figure 5.7 In the MAXILLA, the premaxillomaxillary suture is shown more distinctly than in the drawing. The lucency in the area of the bony palate demonstrates the nasal chamber in comparison with surrounding bone.

The dental buds are conspicuous, with the dense opacity of the enamel caps contrasting with the lucency of adjacent dental pulp and the surrounding crypt.

The palatal process of the PALATINE appears as a homogeneous transverse area. Its lateral extension is demarcated from the medial pterygoid process by a suture.

The pterygoid apparatus is the only sphenoid element in this section. The lateral and the medial pterygoid processes are demonstrated as exaggerations with a common opacity. The PTERYGOID bone is not separately distinguishable.

The EXOCCIPITAL is sectioned through the condyloid process on the right and through the hypoglossal canal on the left. The variable condyloid canal is distinguishable on either side of this specimen.

The BASIOCCIPITAL and the SUPRAOCCIPITAL are in perspective.

The course of the carotid canal within the medial portion of the PETROSAL is shown on the left. On the right, its emergence from the apex of the PETROSAL is shown and also an area of lucency at the opening of the canal on the inferior aspect of the PETROSAL.

The ANNULUS is distinct. The body of the MALLEUS is indistinctly seen on the right.

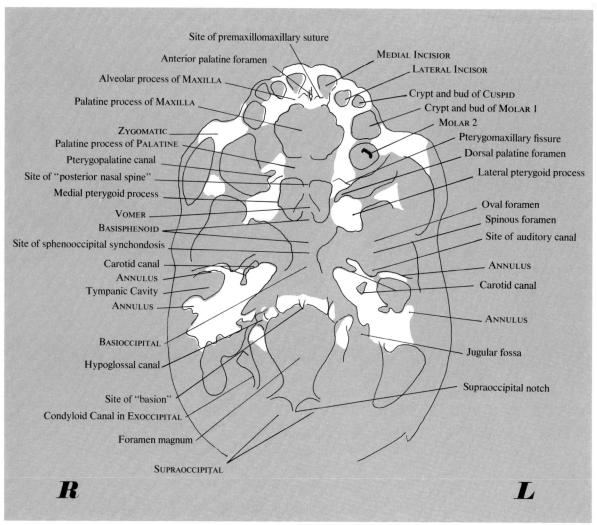

76

Figure 5.7

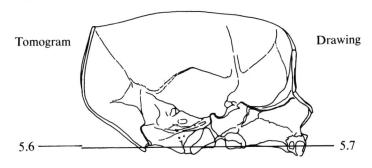

Tomogram

Drawing

5.6 ——————— 5.7

This first transverse anatomical section should be examined in comparison with the photograph of the cranium from its inferior aspect (Figure 5.3) and with the ventral reference cranium drawing, Figure 3.3. There is a lateral asymmetry in this section: the anatomical right (R) being slightly inferior to the left (L) side.

This section shows the unerupted decidual teeth on each side of the MAXILLA; MOLAR I (R) has been lost. The dental crypts are rounded in internal contour; their walls are thin and delicate; the partition between the MOLAR crypts on the right is incomplete. The external walls of the left CUSPID and MOLAR I crypts are broken. The suture demarcating the PREMAXILLA, bearing the INCISORS, is faintly visible in the transsected alveolar bone. Fine perforations are indicated

in the cribriform area of the palatine process; the bone which has developed more recently is streaked radially.

Both the palatine processes and the lateral processes of the PALATINE are well shown. The lateral process, transsected at its base, extends along the lateral aspect of the junction of the nasal chamber and pharynx, at the posterior choanae.

The BASISPHENOID is seen in perspective, between the VOMER, anteriorly, the sphenooccipital synchondrosis, posteriorly, and the medial pterygoid processes, the PTERYGOID bone and the ALISPHENOID, laterally.

The PTERYGOID on the right is sectioned slightly superior to the hamulus; note its sutural junction with the medial pterygoid process. The lateral pterygoid process is also sectioned on the right. The section on the left, at slightly superior level, is through the ALISPHENOID superior to the origin of the lateral pterygoid process.

The EXOCCIPITAL is sectioned through the hypoglossal foramen and, on the left, also through the condyloid canal, which is inconstant among different specimens.

The mass of the PETROSAL borders the anterior lacerated foramen on its anterior aspect and the jugular fossa on its posterior aspect. Buried portion of the styloid process and the stylomastoid portions of the facial canal are approximated in cross-section in the mastoid process.

The anterior flange of the ANNULUS extends along the PETROSAL.

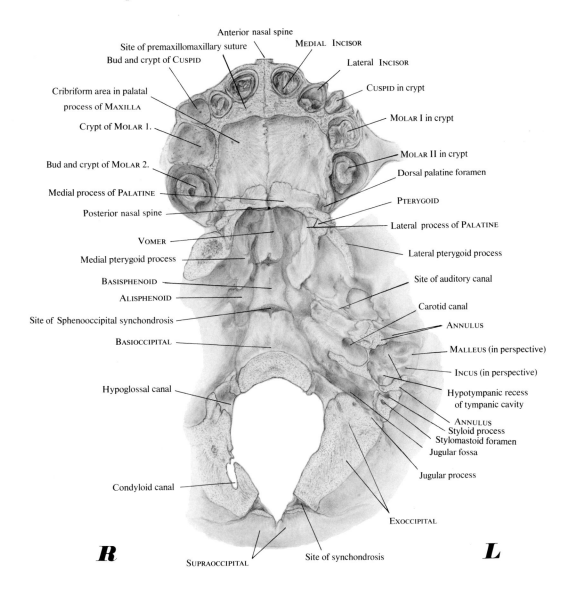

Figure 5.8

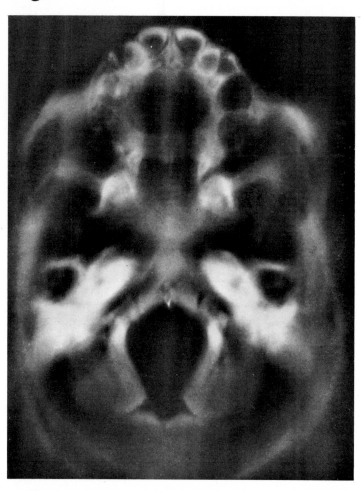

The elements of the MAXILLA closely resemble those shown in the tomogram of Figure 5.6, 1.mm inferior. The premaxillomaxillary suture is more distinct. The maxillopalatine suture at the posterior end of the alveolar ridge can also be discerned. The decidual teeth and their crypts are similar to those in Figure 5.6. The bud of the permanent CUSPID is now shown on the right.

The median suture between the palatal processes of the PALATINE is distinct. The pterygomaxillary fissure is better shown on the left, in the area of the pterygopalatine suture.

The pterygoid processes closely resemble those in Figure 5.6. The EXOCCIPITAL is sectioned through the hypoglossal canal on each side, posterior to the synchondrosis between the BASIOCCIPITAL and EXOCCIPITAL and anterior to the condyle. The inferior margin of the BASIOCCIPITAL is in perspective; the reference point "basion" is indicated by a curved wire. The inferior margin of the SUPRAOCCIPITAL is in perspective.

The densely opaque ANNULUS outlines the tympanic cavity; this section is at the level of the hypotympanic recess. The area of the oval window is indicated by a lucency in the PETROSAL. The curved channel of the carotid canal is visible in the medial portion of the PETROSAL, with a lucent slot at its penetration of the apex.

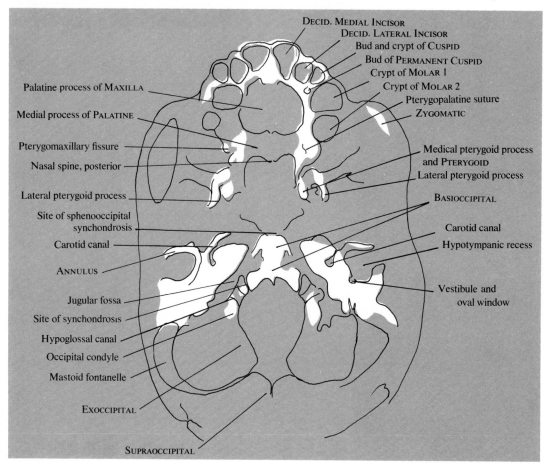

Figure 5.9

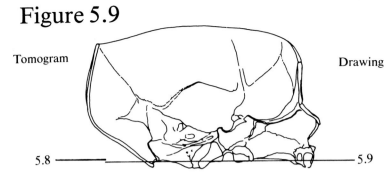

Tomogram

Drawing

5.8 ——————————— 5.9

The left side of this transverse section is 1–2 mm. inferior to the right. The section on the right is precisely through the thin cribriform portion of the palatine process of the MAXILLA, while that on the left is immediately inferior to it.

The INCISORs and their crypts are sectioned through their bases on the right, and through the apices of their crypts on the left. The bud of the PERMANENT MEDIAL INCISOR is shown on the left. The MOLARs which are present (R2 and L1 and 2) are sectioned through their crowns.

The lateral process of the PALATINE is well shown on each side of the posterior choanae. The processes extend posteriorward to the medial pterygoid process. Between the lateral process and the MAXILLA is the groove of the pterygomaxillary fissure, which is continued inferiorly as the posterior palatine foramen (see 5.7).

The inferior aspect of the BASISPHENOID is shown in perspective. On each side, the pterygoid process is demarcated by suture from the ALISPHENOID. The ALISPHENOID is sectioned through its ventral portion. The oval and spinous foramena are not yet separated by skeleton.

In the center of the sectioned BASIOCCIPITAL is a curved channel about the vestige of the notochord. The EXOCCIPITAL is sectioned through the hypoglossal canal on each side and through a margin of the condyloid canal on the left. The SUPRAOCCIPITAL is sectioned through its chondrally-derived inferior portion, superior to its median fissure; a shallow notch, continuing this fissure, is seen on its posterior aspect.

The PETROSAL margins the anterior lacerated foramen and the jugular fossa. At this level, the carotid canal is oblique within the anterior margin of the bone, adjacent to the site of the auditory canal. The basal whorl of the cochlea is shown and also the extension of the labyrinth toward the round window.

The ANNULUS outlines the hypotympanic recess of the tympanic cavity. The junction of the tympanic cavity with the auditory canal is at this level. The promontory over the basal whorl of the cochlea protrudes in the medial wall of the tympanic cavity.

The slender handle of the MALLEUS is shown.

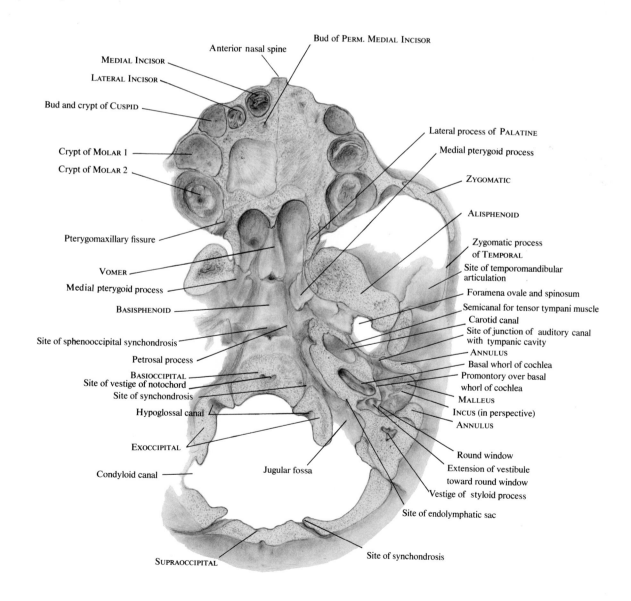

Figure 5.10

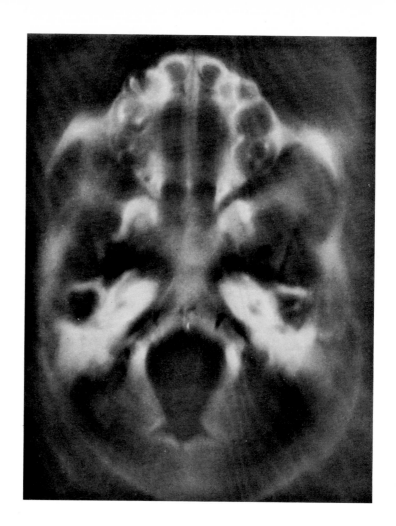

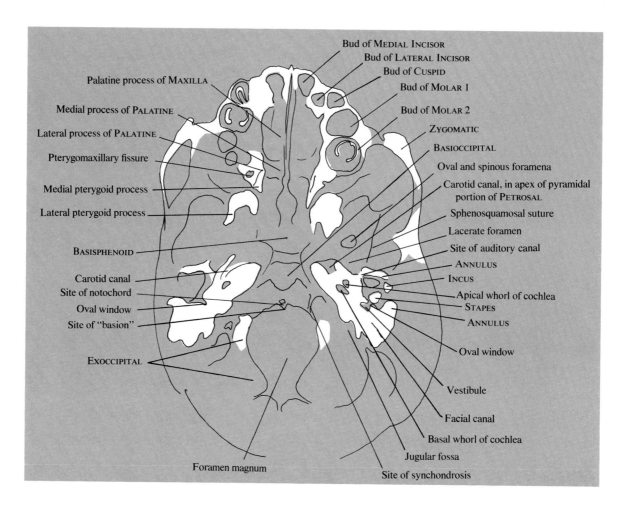

Bud of MEDIAL INCISOR

Bud of LATERAL INCISOR

Bud of CUSPID

Palatine process of MAXILLA

Bud of MOLAR 1

Medial process of PALATINE

Bud of MOLAR 2

Lateral process of PALATINE

ZYGOMATIC

Pterygomaxillary fissure

BASIOCCIPITAL

Oval and spinous foramena

Medial pterygoid process

Carotid canal, in apex of pyramidal
portion of PETROSAL

Lateral pterygoid process

Sphenosquamosal suture

Lacerate foramen

BASISPHENOID

Site of auditory canal

Carotid canal

ANNULUS

Site of notochord

INCUS

Oval window

Apical whorl of cochlea

Site of "basion"

STAPES

ANNULUS

EXOCCIPITAL

Oval window

Vestibule

Facial canal

Basal whorl of cochlea

Foramen magnum

Jugular fossa

Site of synchondrosis

Tomogram

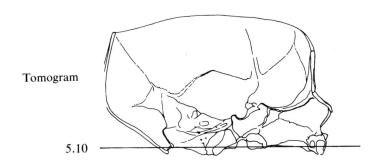

5.10

This tomogram is through the palatine processes of the MAX-ILLA; the median suture of these processes is discernable against the opacity of the base of the VOMER.

The INCISORs and the right CUSPID are sectioned through their bases.

The palatal process of the PALATINE is sectioned at its superior margin. The lateral process is demarcated by the pterygopalatine suture. The pterygopalatine canal is best shown on the right.

The lateral and medial pterygoid processes are radiographically sectioned near their base, and less sharply outlined. The combined oval and spinous foramena are well outlined.

The irregular lucency seen in the center of the BASIOCCIPITAL probably corresponds with the vestige of the notochord found at this site (see Fig. 5.9). The site of the synchondrosis between the BASIOCCIPITAL and EXOCCIPITAL is distinct on the right. The site "basion" is marked with a piece of wire.

The emergence of the carotid canal from the apex of the PETROSAL is indicated by a notch. The lucency of the cochlea is discernable adjacent to that of the carotid canal within the PETROSAL.

The hypotympanic recess is in this plane; the extension of this recess toward the round window is seen on each side. The body of the MALLEUS is seen indistinctly, on the right.

Figure 5.11

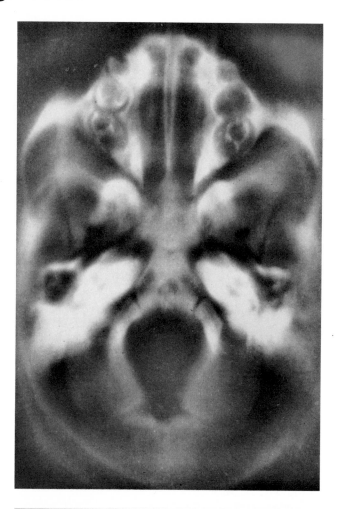

In the alveolar portion of the MAXILLA are the crypts of the MEDIAL INCISORs, and the buds and crypts of the PERMANENT LATERAL INCISORs. The MOLARs and their crypts are as in Fig. 5.10. The orbital process is now shown. And the maxillozygomatic suture on the right.

The lateral process of the PALATINE is well demarcated by the pterygopalatine suture on each side. The pterygomaxillary fissure is better demonstrated on the left.

This is the most inferior level at which the VOMER can be distinguished: as a median strip, overlying the median suture of the palatine processes of the PALATINE, and as paramedian opaque lines, of the lateral processes.

The pterygoid processes are radiographically indistinct, at their junction with the ALISPHENOID.

This section is at the superior margin of distinct delineation of the foramen magnum. The central lucency in the BASIOCCIPITAL at the site of the embryonal notochord is expanded into a less distinct area. The EXOCCIPITALs are sectioned superior to the hypoglossal canal.

The carotid canal appears as a notch in the anterior aspect of the apex of the PETROSAL. The cochlea and the extension of the vestibule toward the round window are shown as subtly marginned lucencies within it. The cochlea is marginally distinct. The lateral arch of the lateral semicircular canal is well shown. The carotid canal is less distinct.

The site of the auditory canal is delineated in this section, at its junction with the tympanic cavity. The anterior portion of the ANNULUS is conspicuous. The body of the MALLEUS and of the INCUS are marginally distinct.

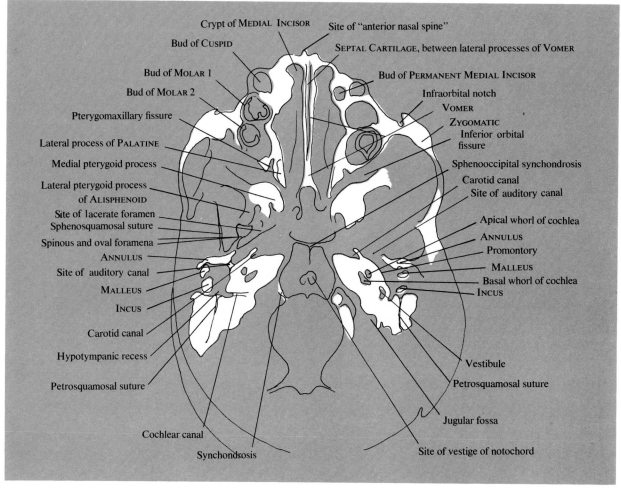

Figure 5.12

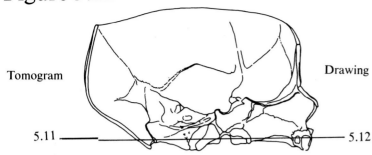

Tomogram

Drawing

5.11 ——————————— 5.12

The MOLAR portion of the maxillary alveolar process is located between the nasal chamber and the pterygoid space, and inferior to the orbit. The maxilloethmoidal suture is fused at this transverse plane, though the thin lateral wall is distinguished from the MAXILLA in the corresponding tomogram (see Figures 5.10 and 5.11.

The INFERIOR CONCHAE appear in this specimen only as simple curved flanges; their scroll-like peripheral portions were lost in the preparation.

The lateral process of the PALATINE is shown in its posteriorward extent on the left. On the right, its extension toward the medial pterygoid process and the separate PTERYGOID is interrupted.

The thin paramedian processes of the VOMER margin the SEPTAL CARTILAGE; these show postmortem distortions of form. The anterior tip of the VOMER is lost in the preparation. Posteriorly, the VOMER continues as a curved shelf, extended lateralward by symmetrical alae.

The apical and basal whorls of the cochlea are shown on each side. On the left, the basal whorl bulges into the tympanic cavity as the promontory. On the left the vestibule extends toward the round window.

All of the OSSICLES are represented at this level on the right. The handle of the MALLEUS is seen in cross section. The long process of the INCUS articulates with STAPES. STAPES is shown entirely: the head (at the articulation), the 2 crura, and the footplate, in the oval window.

The BASIOCCIPITAL is arch-shaped in this section; the median notch in its dorsal margin and a faint median line in the cancellous bone indicates the site of fusion of bone derived from the 2 paramedian hemicenters. Only the limb of each EXOCCIPITAL superior to the hypoglossal canal is shown. The portion of the SUPRAOCCIPITAL derived is chondral in origin.

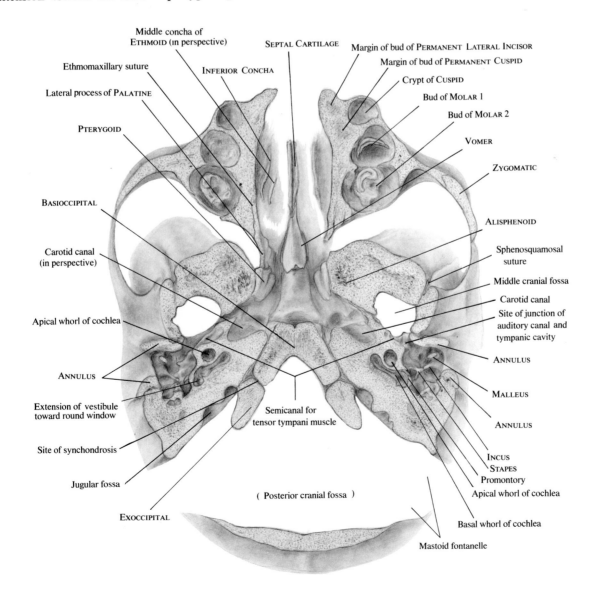

Figure 5.13

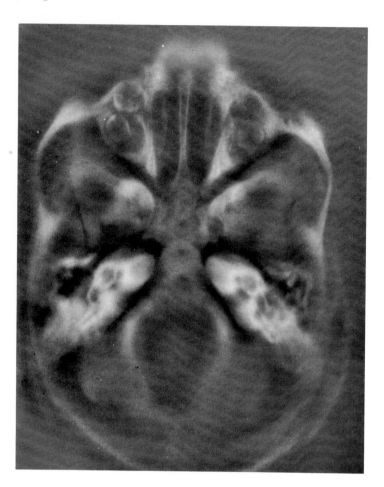

In this tomogram, the MAXILLA on either side consists of the alveolar and the orbital processes, the latter extending lateralward to the ZYGOMATIC. Within the alveolar process are the bud of the PERMANENT CUSPID, and the buds of the DECIDUAL MOLARs and their crypts.

The lateral process of the PALATINE is well demarcated from the MAXILLA; the pterygomaxillary fissure is shown on the left.

The VOMER is sectioned through its paramedian vertical processes and alae.

The lateral wall of the ETHMOID is demarcated from the MAXILLA, particularly on the right. The portion of the INFERIOR CONCHAE are best distinguished as that portion of their scroll-like contour which extends vertically from the transverse base.

The ALISPHENOID and BASISPHENOID are broadly separated at their suture, shown here on the right.

In this and in more superior radiographic sections, only the posterior rim of the SUPRAOCCIPITAL is shown.

The internal acoustic meatus slightly indents the PETROSAL on the left, but is shown in most of its length on the right. Within the PETROSAL, the apical whorl of the cochlea is demonstrated on each side. The vestibule and the inferior limb of the semicircular canal are shown on the left. These and part of the lateral semicircular canal are shown on the right.

The MALLEUS is shown indistinctly on the left and distinctly on the right. The INCUS and STAPES are a continuous opacity on the right.

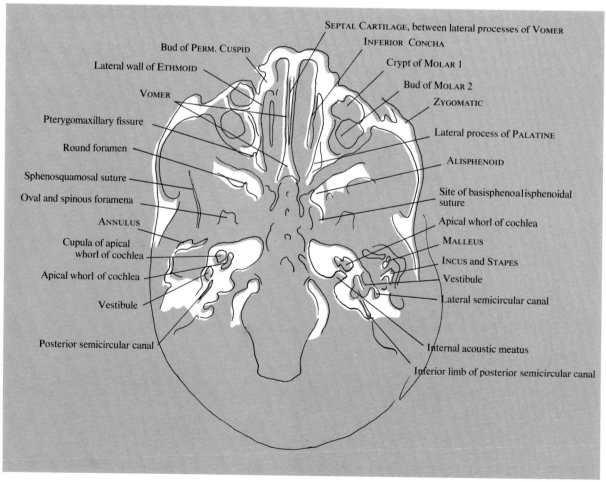

Figure 5.14

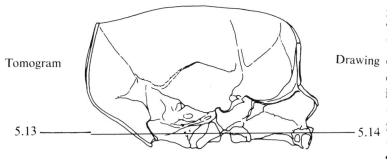

Tomogram

Drawing

5.13 ——————————— 5.14

The MAXILLA is a triangular block containing the bud of DECID. MOLAR 2 and its crypt and the margin of the crypt of MOLAR 1. It is fused with the ETHMOID except posteriorly, where the suture is still evident. Note the approximation of the MOLAR 2 crypt to the pterygoid fossa; the bony enclosure at this margin is incomplete.

On the left, the lateral process of the PALATINE extends medialward to the lateral wing of the VOMER, at the top of the posterior choanae. This extension is interrupted on the right. The pterygo-maxillary fissure is evident on the left between the PALATINE and the MAXILLA; at this level, a small foramen penetrates to the nasal chamber.

The ALISPHENOID is sectioned near the round foramen.

The rostrum of the BASISPHENOID is penetrated by the bony canal about the tract of the embryonal craniopharyngeal pouch. In this specimen, the further course of this pouch through the BASISPHENOID is not well-demonstrated, and is omitted from the drawings. The bones of Bertin are transient in the fetus and infant, later fusing with the BASISPHENOID. The carotid groove is well outlined between the BASISPHENOID and the PETROSAL.

The semicanal for the tensor tympani muscle indents the PETROSAL on each side. On the left is shown the slender hamulus of the tensor tympani muscle, about which the tendon turns to descend to the MALLEUS. The footplate of the STAPES, the oval window and adjacent extension of the vestibule are shown on the left. The whorls of the cochlea and the inferior curve of the posterior semicircular canal are shown on each side. The facial canal is well demarcated, posterior to the tympanic cavity. The medial wall of the tympanic cavity contains the oval window (shown on the left), the promontory, and the extension of the tympanic recess toward the round window. Its lateral wall is part of the SQUAMOSAL.

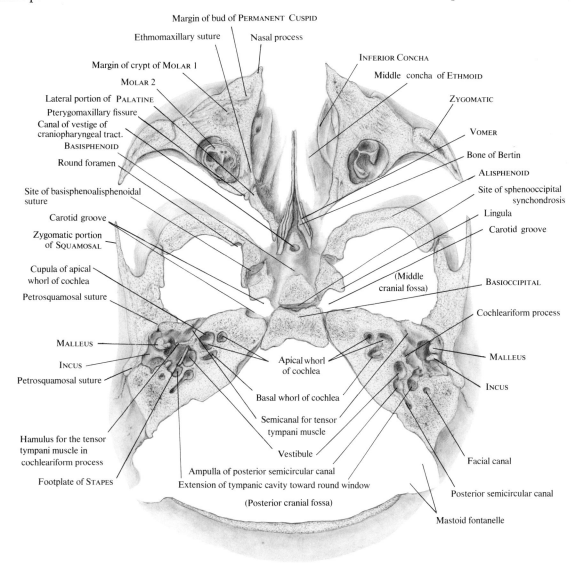

Margin of bud of PERMANENT CUSPID
Ethmomaxillary suture
Nasal process
Margin of crypt of MOLAR 1
MOLAR 2
Lateral portion of PALATINE
Pterygomaxillary fissure
Canal of vestige of craniopharyngeal tract.
BASISPHENOID
Round foramen
Site of basisphenoalisphenoidal suture
Carotid groove
Zygomatic portion of SQUAMOSAL
Cupula of apical whorl of cochlea
Petrosquamosal suture
MALLEUS
INCUS
Petrosquamosal suture
Hamulus for the tensor tympani muscle in cochleariform process
Footplate of STAPES

INFERIOR CONCHA
Middle concha of ETHMOID
ZYGOMATIC
VOMER
Bone of Bertin
ALISPHENOID
Site of sphenooccipital synchondrosis
Lingula
Carotid groove
(Middle cranial fossa)
BASIOCCIPITAL
Cochleariform process
MALLEUS
INCUS
Facial canal
Posterior semicircular canal
Mastoid fontanelle

Apical whorl of cochlea
Basal whorl of cochlea
Semicanal for tensor tympani muscle
Vestibule
Ampulla of posterior semicircular canal
Extension of tympanic cavity toward round window
(Posterior cranial fossa)

Figure 5.15

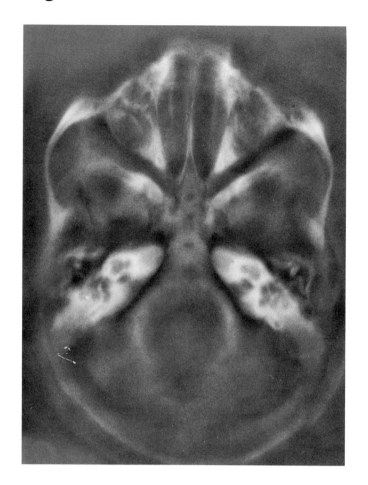

The left MAXILLA contains the buds of the two DECIDUAL MOLARs. In the right MAXILLA, at a slightly superior level, the inferior portion of the maxillary sinus is seen.

The lateral process of the PALATINE extends as a spur posteromedially from the combined mass of MAXILLA and ETHMOID.

In this section, the alae of the VOMER are separated, on either side of the rostrum of the BASISPHENOID.

The round foramen and the sphenosquamosal suture are shown in the ALISPHENOID on each side.

The carotid groove is well distinguished beside the BASI-SPHENOID on each side.

The superior portion of the internal acoustic meatus is outlined by the PETROSAL. This is separated from the lucency of the apical whorl of the cochlea. On the left, the vestibule is in continuity with the inferior limb of the posterior semicircular canal; on the right, the posterior portion of the posterior canal is sectioned at the posterolateral margin of the PETROSAL, and the superior limb of this canal is shown at its junction with the vestibule. The fossa of the endolymphatic sac lies between these two portions of the canal. On the left, the lateral semi-circular canal is in continuity with the vestibule. The hiatus of the facial canal is shown as an indentation on the anterior aspect of the PETROSAL on each side.

The MALLEUS and the combined opacity of INCUS and STAPES are shown on each side.

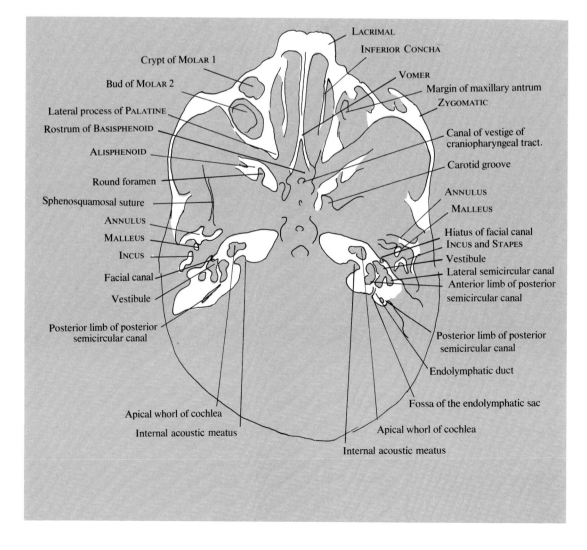

Figure 5.16

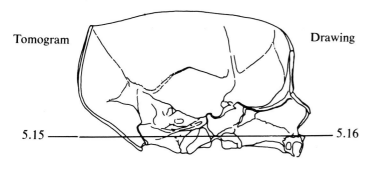

Tomogram   Drawing

5.15 ——————————— 5.16

At this level, the MAXILLA contains the superior margin of the bud of MOLAR 2. The ethmomaxillary suture is more evident than in the sections inferior to this. The margin of the orifice of the infraorbital canal is shown on either side.

The lateral process of the PALATINE is shown on either side; it is approximated by the INFERIOR CONCHA.

As the lateral wings (alae) of the VOMER are sectioned, they are shaped as prongs; the bones of Bertin are in continuity with either wing, in approximation to the rostrum of the BASISPHENOID.

Sutural demarcation of the lateral wall of the ETHMOID from the MAXILLA is best shown at this transverse level.

The INFERIOR CONCHA, which is derived separately from the ETHMOID, is shown in much of its length. Posterior and medial to it is the middle concha. The ALISPHENOID is sectioned in its vertical portion, at the level of the round foramen. Each ALISPHENOID is closely approximated to the BASISPHENOID at this level.

This section of the PETROSAL on either side is through the vestibule, the basal whorl of the cochlea and the posterior semicircular canal. A margin of the basal and apical whorls is also shown on the left.

The epitympanic recess of the tympanic cavity is enclosed by the PETROSAL and SQUAMOSAL. It contains the head of the MALLEUS and the body of the INCUS. The base of the hamulus of the tensor tympani muscle is shown on the left. The fine bony laminae of the pyramid about the stapedius muscle are shown on the right.

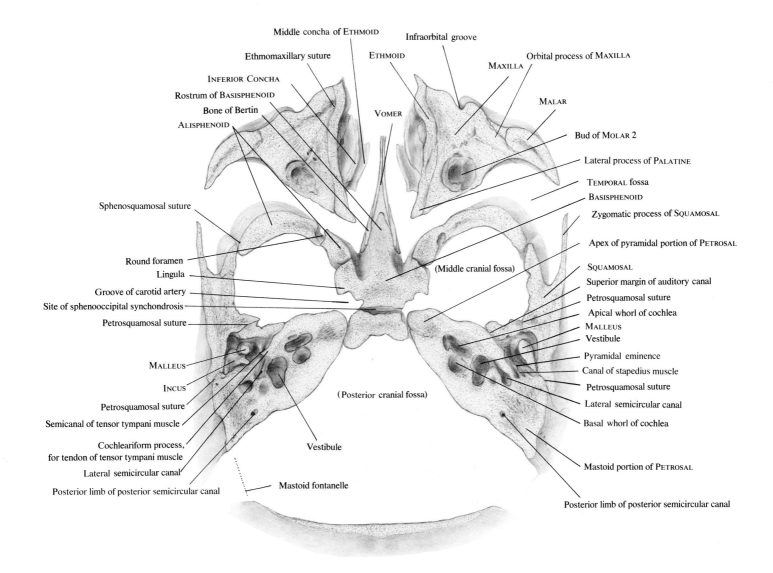

Figure 5.17

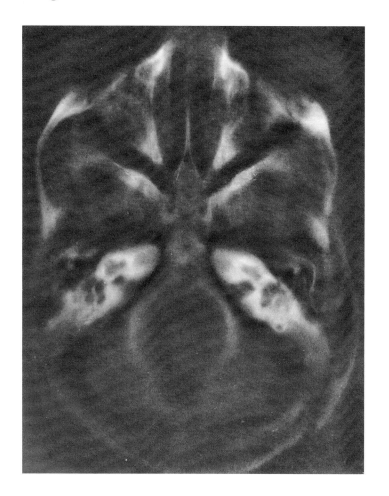

The **MAXILLA** encloses the superior portion of the bud of **MOLAR 2**, the bud of **PERMANENT MOLAR 1**, and the inferior margin of the maxillary antrum. The orifice of the infraorbital canal and a portion of the canal are also shown. The **ALISPHENOID** is sectioned through the round foramen on the left.

In the **BASISPHENOID**, the orifice of the residual bony tract about the embryonal craniopharyngeal pouch is shown as a discrete round lucency.

In the **PETROSAL**, the cochlea is well distinguished on the left. The medial portion of the left internal acoustic meatus is indistinct. The vestibule and the adjacent portions of the semicircular canals appear as a large lucency in the **PETROSAL**. Only the verticle portion of the **ANNULUS** is well delineated on the left. The footplate of the **STAPES** is distinct on the right.

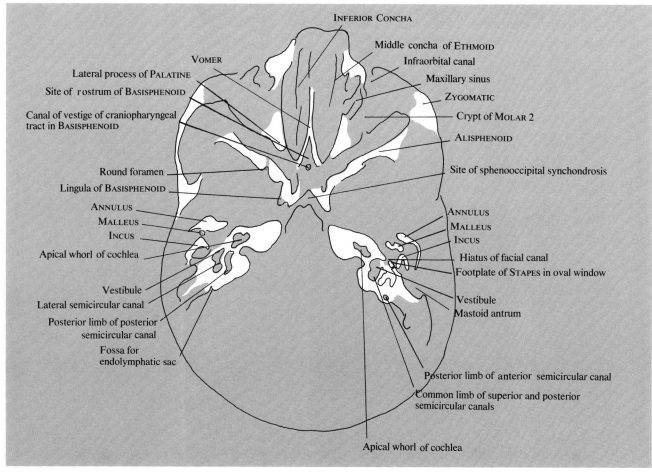

Figure 5.19

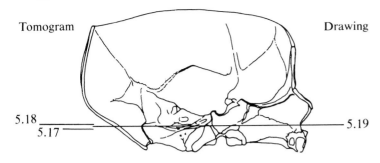

Tomogram   Drawing

5.18
5.17 ———————————————— 5.19

This is the superior level of the tooth-containing part of the MAXILLA: the superior margin of the crypt of MOLAR 2 is shown on the left. On the left, the maxillary sinus is shown in continuity from the middle meatus through its penetration of the ETHMOID wall and into the MAXILLA. The inferior margin of the sinus is shown on the right, adjacent to the ethmomaxillary suture.

The infraorbital canal is shown in full width on the right, and a portion of its orifice is shown on the left. The lateral wall of the ETHMOID is suturally demarcated from the MAXILLA anterior to the antrum.

The INFERIOR CONCHA, which is separate from the ETHMOID in its derivation, joins it at a discrete suture.

The VOMER is again shown as a continuity of narrow paramedian processes, each diverging lateralward toward the sides of the rostrum of the BASISPHENOID.

At this level, the BASISPHENOID and ALISPHENOID are well approximated. The ALISPHENOID is penetrated by the round foramen on the right.

The tract about the vestige of the embryonal craniopharyngeal pouch is indistinct inside of the BASISPHENOID and is omitted from the illustration.

The superior lip of the BASIOCCIPITAL is slightly asymmetrical, giving erroneous impression of mechanical displacement.

The PETROSAL is sectioned through the internal acoustic meatus, the vestibule, the cochlea and the posterior limb of the posterior semicircular canal. On the right, the facial canal is open on the anterior aspect of the PETROSAL. On the left, the course of the canal medial to the tympanic cavity is shown.

The epitympanic recess is smaller than in Figure 5.16 and is smoothly walled. It contains the head of the MALLEUS and the body of the INCUS.

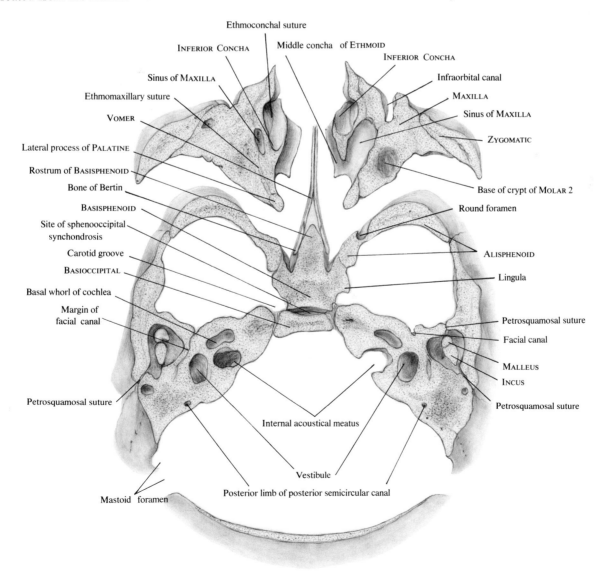

Figure 5.18

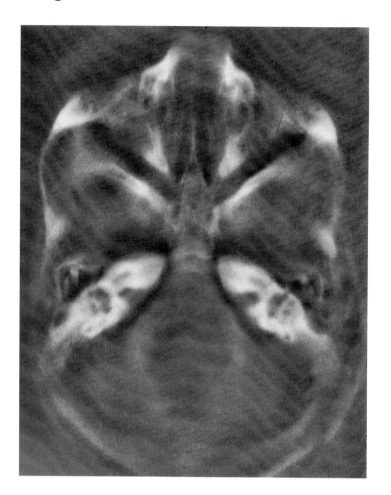

At this level, the MAXILLA contains the superior margin of the crypt of MOLAR 2 and a larger portion of the maxillary antrum. A greater extent of the infraorbital canal is also shown.

The wings of the VOMER are shown as narrow opacities on either side of the BASISPHENOID.

The ALISPHENOID is sectioned through its vertical portion on each side.

Within the BASISPHENOID, the interior of the rostrum anterior to the tract about the embryonal craniopharyngeal pouch is irregularly lucent.

The vertical portion of the posterior semicircular canal is a discrete radiolucency bounded ventromedially by the shallow excavation of the endolymphatic sac. The apical whorl of the cochlea is in focus near the anterolateral margin of the internal acoustic meatus. The hiatus of the facial canal is seen immediately lateral to the apical whorl of the cochlea on the right. The superior portion of the ANNULUS, the MALLEUS and the INCUS are distinct.

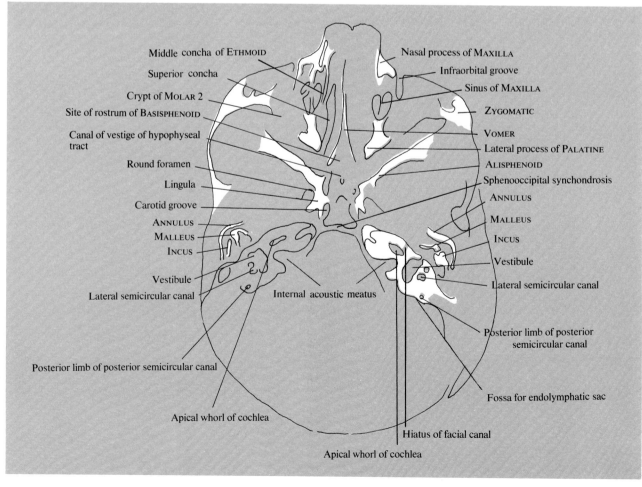

Figure 5.19

See legend on page 89.

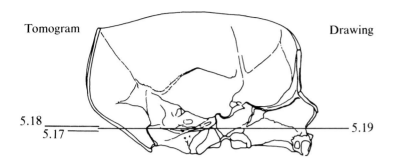

Tomogram

Drawing

5.18
5.17
5.19

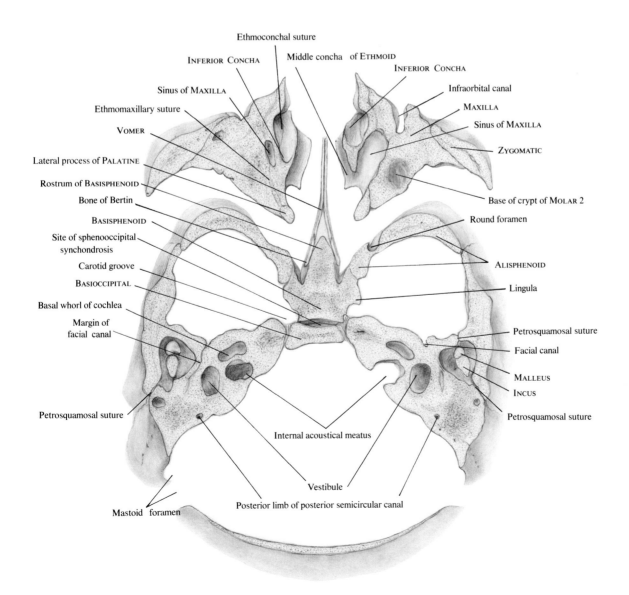

Ethmoconchal suture

INFERIOR CONCHA

Middle concha of ETHMOID

INFERIOR CONCHA

Sinus of MAXILLA

Infraorbital canal

Ethmomaxillary suture

MAXILLA

VOMER

Sinus of MAXILLA

Lateral process of PALATINE

ZYGOMATIC

Rostrum of BASISPHENOID

Bone of Bertin

Base of crypt of MOLAR 2

BASISPHENOID

Round foramen

Site of sphenooccipital
synchondrosis

Carotid groove

ALISPHENOID

BASIOCCIPITAL

Lingula

Basal whorl of cochlea

Margin of
facial canal

Petrosquamosal suture

Facial canal

MALLEUS

INCUS

Petrosquamosal suture

Petrosquamosal suture

Internal acoustical meatus

Vestibule

Mastoid foramen

Posterior limb of posterior semicircular canal

Figure 5.20

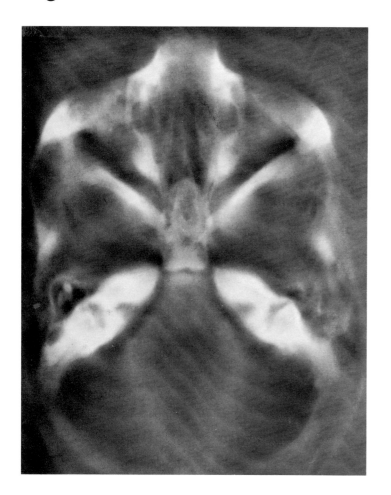

The sinus occupies much of the central area of the MAXILLA. Lateral to this, the MAXILLA constitutes the floor of the orbit; the infraorbital groove is distinguised within it.

This is the most superior radiographic level at which the lateral wings (alae) of the VOMER are distinguished.

Radiographically, the conchae appear composed of irregular bone. In contrast, the anatomical sections demonstrate only the simpler primary portions of the conchae, close to their bases.

The ALISPHENOID and BASISPHENOID are separated at the superior orbital fissure.

The tract about the vestige of the embryonal craniopharyngeal pouch is small at this level.

In the PETROSAL, the apical whorl of the cochlea is distinct. The common limb of the posterior and anterior semicircular canals is inseparable from the posterior aspect of the subarcuate fossa on the left. The posterior limb of the posterior semicircular canal is distinct on the left. The MALLEUS and INCUS are distinct on the left, but are a fused opacity on the right.

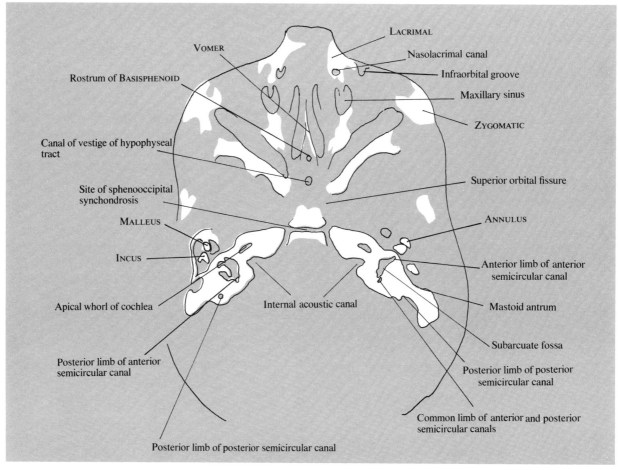

Figure 5.21

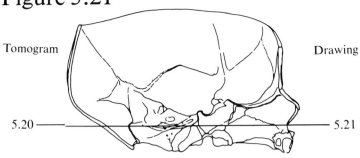

Tomogram   Drawing

5.20 ———————————— 5.21

The wall between the nasal chamber and the orbit is constituted of the MAXILLA. It contains the bud of PERMANENT MOLAR 2. The nasolacrimal canal opens into the nasal cavity at this level, inferior to the INFERIOR CONCHA.

In this specimen, the ethmomaxillary suture is discernable anterior to the nasolacrimal canal.

Most of the complex details of the middle and superior conchae were lost in the anatomical preparation. The superior tip of the lateral process of the PALATINE is discernable at the posterior extremity of the MAXILLA.

The lateral wings of the VOMER are shown at their superior margins.

The ALISPHENOID and BASISPHENOID are separated by the superior orbital fissure.

In the PETROSAL on the left side, the internal acoustic meatus is sectioned obliquely. On the right side, the meatus approximates the vestibule. The full length of the lateral semicircular canals and the adjacent parts of the vestibule are demonstrated on both sides. The prominence of the lateral canals indent the epitympanic recesses. Also shown are the origin of the anterior limb of the anterior semicircular canal and the common crura of the anterior and posterior semicircular canals from the vestibule, and the vertical portion of the posterior semicircular canal. The tip of the apical whorl of the cochlea is shown on the left. The origin of the facial canal from the meatus is shown on the right. The hiatus of the canal, the site of the geniculate ganglion of the facial nerve, is shown on the left.

The epitympanic recess of the tympanic cavity and the antrum are shown. On the lateral aspect of the antrum are small irregular penetrations into the SQUAMOSAL; some of these appear as cells.

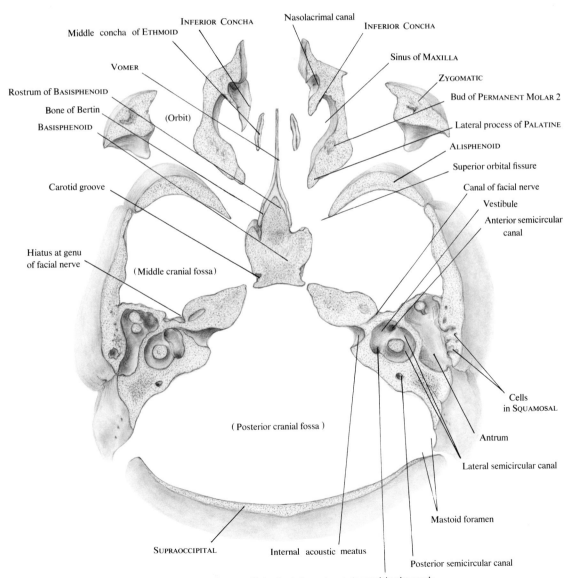

Figure 5.22

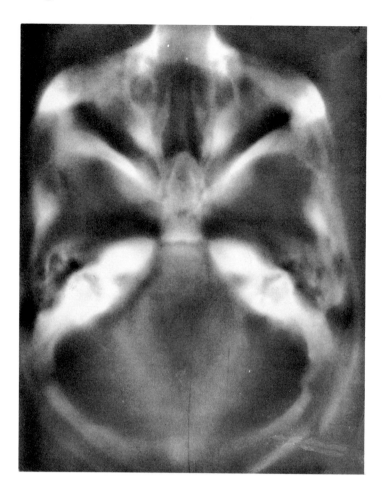

The elements of the MAXILLA at this level are highly similar to those in Figure 5.20.

The medial portion of the ALISPHENOID is essentially vertical and, hence, radiopaque.

The ventral portion of the BASISPHENOID is conical in radiographic form, with irregular internal lucency. Its posterior portion is essentially square.

Within the PETROSAL, the anterior semicircular canal and the subarcuate fossa are in continuity. The medial portion of the internal acoustic meatus is sharply outlined. The epitympanic recess of the tympanic cavity is well seen on each side. But the ossicles are indistinct on the left and not visualized on the right.

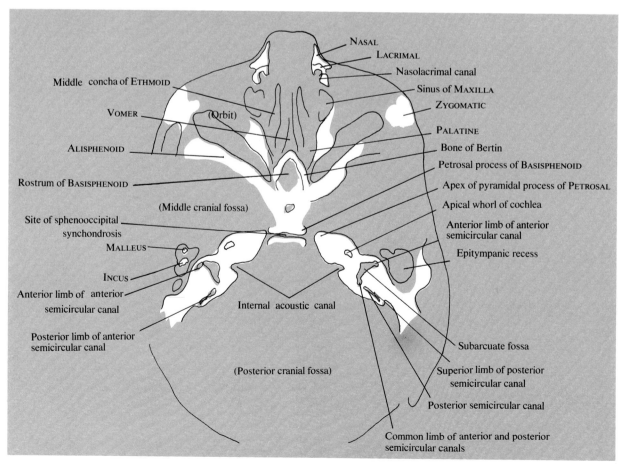

Figure 5.23

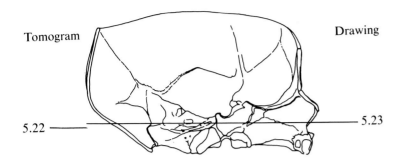

Tomogram

Drawing

5.22 ——————————————— 5.23

The nasal chamber and the orbit are separated by the ETHMOID, which is indented by the maxillary sinus and the nasolacrimal canal. The sinus and canal are continuous on the right; the nasolacrimal canal is a separately enclosed cavity on the left.
The ALISPHENOID is a simple arch in section.
The BASISPHENOID is block-like in its posterior portion and tapered anteriorly. Its apex is enclosed by the bones of Bertin and by tips of the wings of the VOMER.

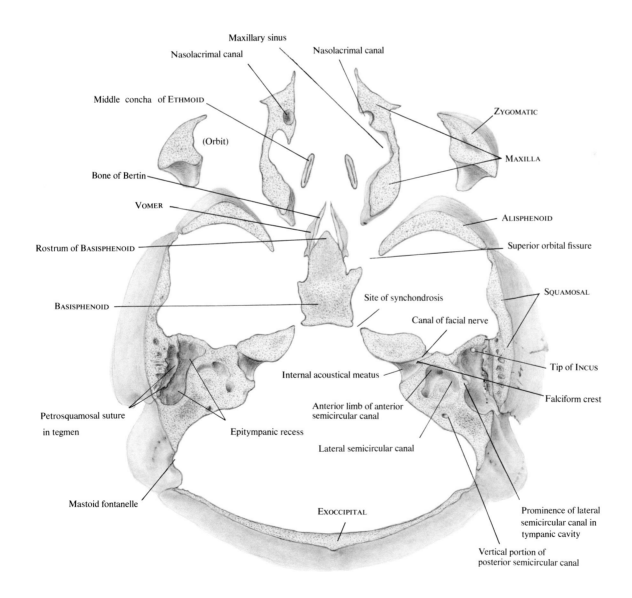

Figure 5.24

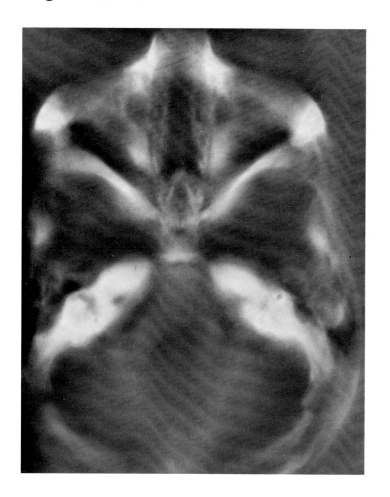

The orbital margin of the MAXILLA and the contour of the maxillary antrum within the fused ETHMOID and MAXILLA are highly similar to those in Figure 5.22. The nasolacrimal canal is located slightly more lateral than in Figure 5.23, and is further separated from the nasal chamber.

This is the level of the posterior attachment of the middle concha. This attachment is broad, and its bone is irregularly opaque.

The ALISPHENOID and BASISPHENOID are further separated by the superior orbital fissure.

The anterior limb of the anterior semicircular canal is well demonstrated; the posterior limb is out of this plane. The tympanic cavity is sectioned through the epitympanic recess.

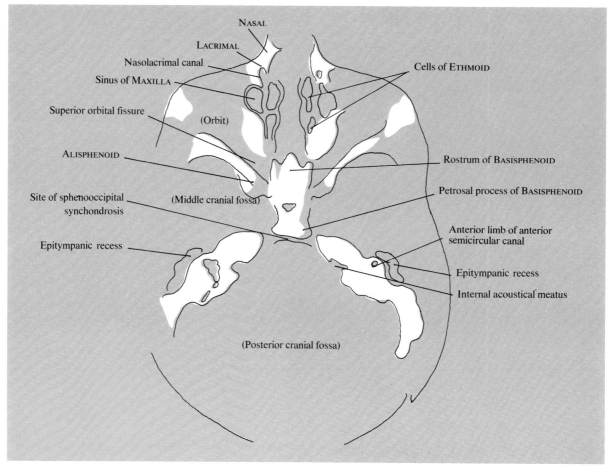

Figure 5.25

Tomogram 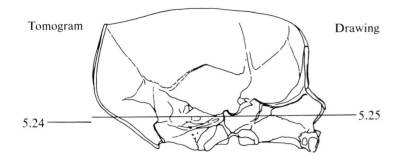 Drawing

5.24 ——————————————— 5.25

The MAXILLA and ETHMOID are a single block, without suture distinction. The maxillary sinus is partially demarcated from the nasal chamber by the base of the middle concha. It is now separated from the orbit by a thin wall.

The nasolacrimal canal is displaced lateralward, farther from the nasal chamber, in comparison with Figure 5.24. The ethmoidal cells are distinguished in the posterior portion of this mass.

The ALISPHENOID approximates the MALAR.

The portion of the BASISPHENOID is immediately inferior to the hypophyseal recess.

In the PETROSAL at this level, the bony labyrinth is represented by the common limbs of the posterior and anterior semicircular canals, by the superior curve of the posterior semicircular canal and by the anterior limb of the anterior semicircular canal.

This section is at the superiormost portion of the epitympanic recess. Its medial aspect is smooth. But its lateral aspect is irregularly penetrated by cells of the SQUAMOSAL.

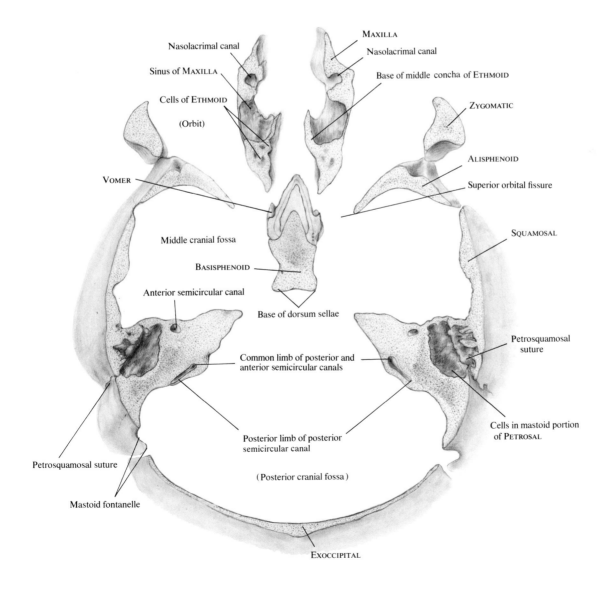

Figure 5.26

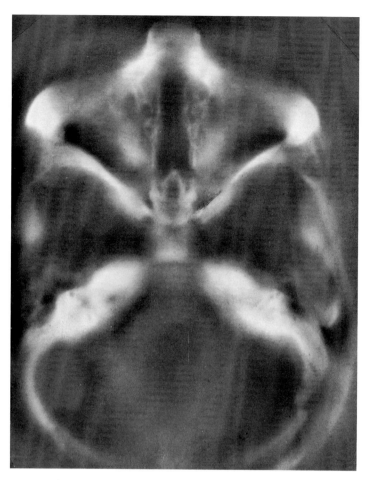

The mass separating the nasal chambers and the orbit is probably of ETHMOID. The maxillary antrum extends nearly to the orbit. The nasolacrimal canal is skeletally enclosed.
As is Figure 5.24, the conchae are irregular opacities.
The BASISPHENOID is indented by the hypophyseal fossa. A lucency in the anterior wall of the fossa indicates the orifice of the tract about the embryonal hypophyseal pouch.
The subarcuate fossa and the vertical portions of the anterior semicircular canals are distinct within the PETROSAL. The tympanic cavity is sectioned at the epitympanic recess.

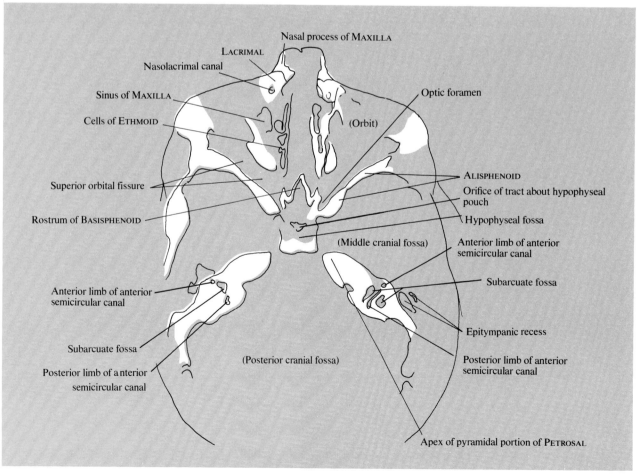

Figure 5.28

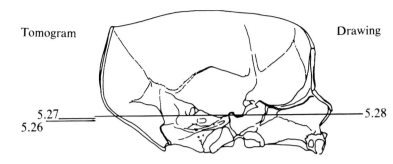

Tomogram   Drawing

5.27
5.26   5.28

The base of the superior concha projects medialward from the ETHMOID.

The nasolacrimal canal is open lateralward.

The dorsum sellae of the BASISPHENOID is chondral. Hence, only the anterior wall of the hypophyseal fossa is demonstrated.

The optic foramen is enclosed by the superior root of the lesser wing, anteriorly, and by the inferior root, posteriorly.

The bony labyrinth within the PETROSAL is represented only by the anterior semicircular canal. In the fetus and infant this canal protrudes from the superior aspect of the PETROSAL in the arcuate crest with the subarcuate fossa, containing dura, extending lateralward below it.

The epitympanic recess is now a cavity in the anterior part of the PETROSAL. The petrosquamosal suture is lateral to the epitympanic recess.

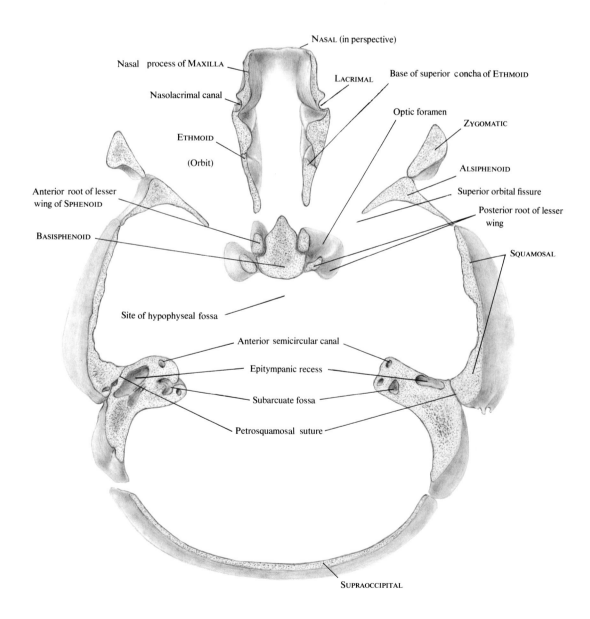

NASAL (in perspective)

Nasal process of MAXILLA

Base of superior concha of ETHMOID

LACRIMAL

Nasolacrimal canal

Optic foramen

ETHMOID

ZYGOMATIC

(Orbit)

ALSIPHENOID

Anterior root of lesser wing of SPHENOID

Superior orbital fissure

Posterior root of lesser wing

BASISPHENOID

SQUAMOSAL

Site of hypophyseal fossa

Anterior semicircular canal

Epitympanic recess

Subarcuate fossa

Petrosquamosal suture

SUPRAOCCIPITAL

Figure 5.27

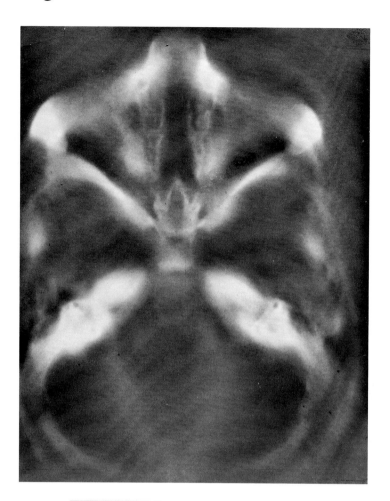

This section is through the superior margin of the maxillary sinus. The ethmoidal cells are now distinguishable in the posterior portion of the ETHMOID.

The scroll pattern of the middle concha is shown.

The nasolacrimal canal is enclosed by the LACRIMAL bone.

The roots of the lesser wing are comparable to their appearance in Figure 5.24.

The limbs of the anterior semicircular canal are distinct on the left. The internal acoustic canal is distinguishable on each side.

The epitympanic recess and the mastoid antrum and adjacent cells are well shown on the right.

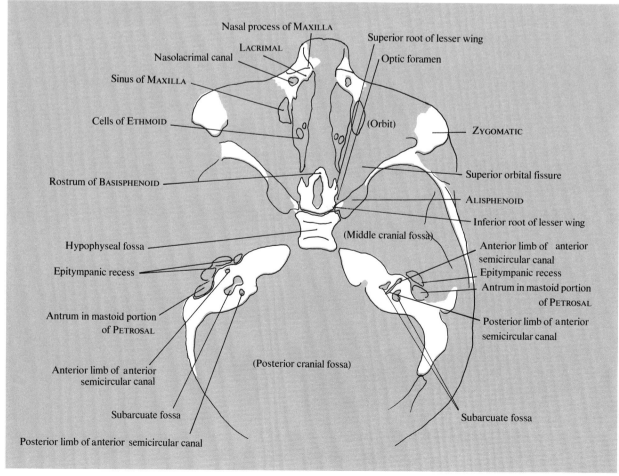

Figure 5.28

See legend on page 99.

Tomogram

Drawing

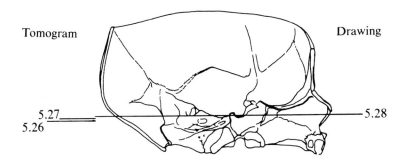

5.27

5.28

5.26

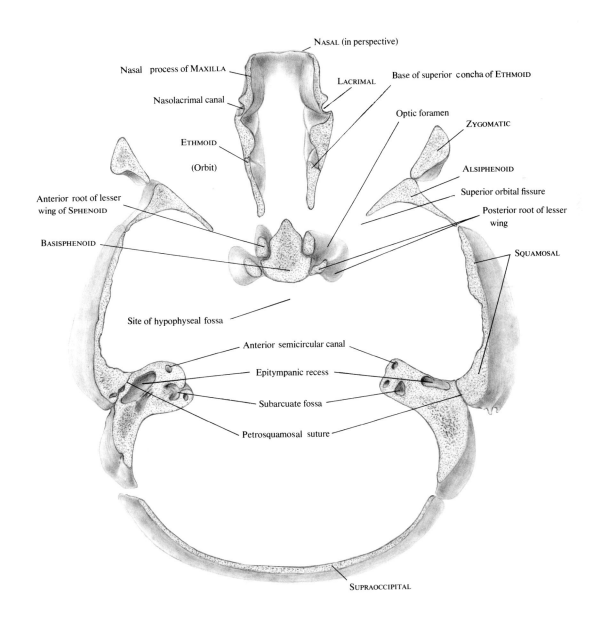

NASAL (in perspective)

Nasal process of MAXILLA

LACRIMAL

Base of superior concha of ETHMOID

Nasolacrimal canal

Optic foramen

ZYGOMATIC

ETHMOID

ALSIPHENOID

(Orbit)

Superior orbital fissure

Anterior root of lesser wing of SPHENOID

Posterior root of lesser wing

BASISPHENOID

SQUAMOSAL

Site of hypophyseal fossa

Anterior semicircular canal

Epitympanic recess

Subarcuate fossa

Petrosquamosal suture

SUPRAOCCIPITAL

Figure 5.29

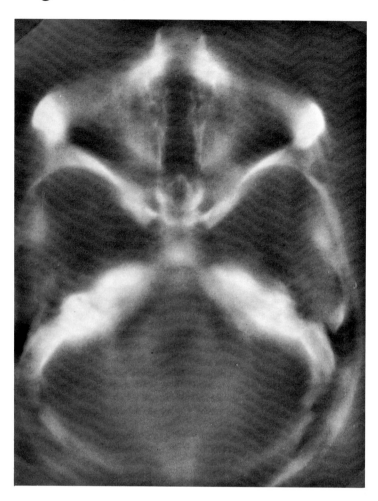

The **ETHMOID** opacity is narrow. The ethmoid cells are distinguishable in its posterior portion.

The **LACRIMAL** encloses the nasolacrimal canal.

In this and in the tomogram of Figure 5.30, the processes of the lesser wing, enclosing the optic foreman, are distinct. The chiasmatic sulcus is distinct.

Of the bony labyrinth within the **PETROSAL**, only the anterior semicircular canal is clearly shown, within the arcuate eminence.

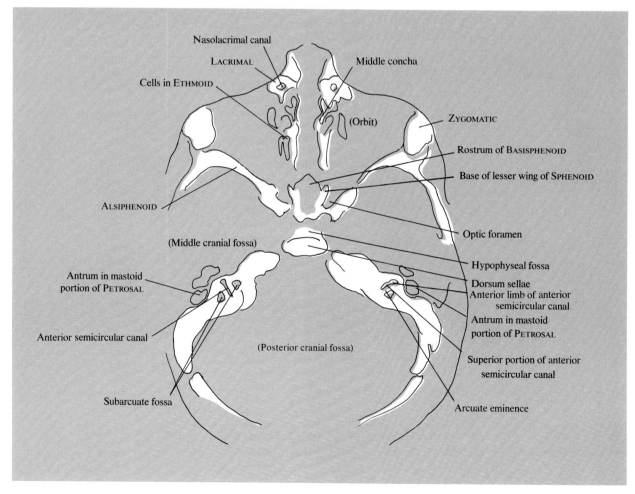

Figure 5.30

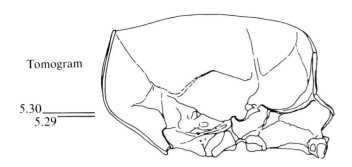

Tomogram

5.30
5.29

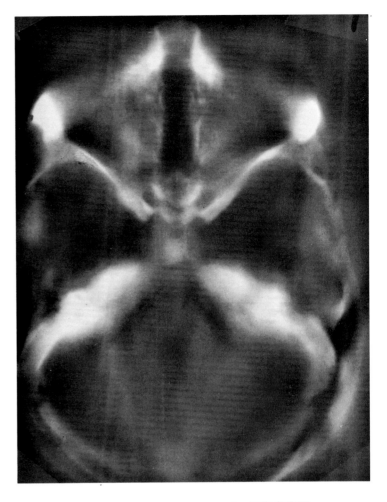

The lateral wall of the ETHMOID is diminished, compared with the tomogram of Figure 5.29.
The nasolacrimal canal is open lateralward.
The crest of the anterior semicircular canal is the only structure clearly seen within the PETROSAL.

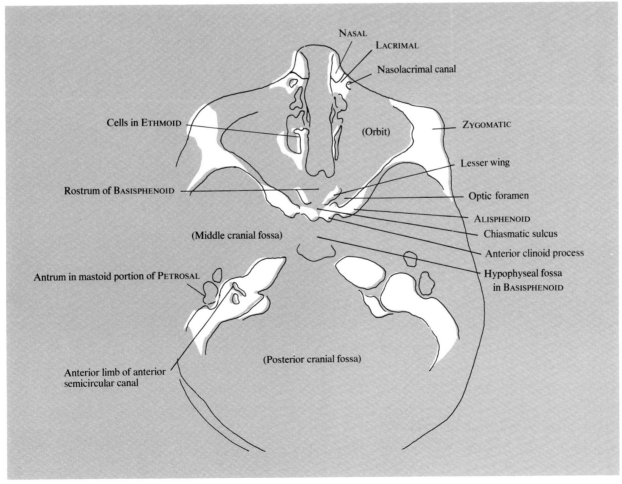

NASAL
LACRIMAL
Nasolacrimal canal
Cells in ETHMOID
(Orbit)
ZYGOMATIC
Lesser wing
Rostrum of BASISPHENOID
Optic foramen
ALISPHENOID
(Middle cranial fossa)
Chiasmatic sulcus
Anterior clinoid process
Antrum in mastoid portion of PETROSAL
Hypophyseal fossa in BASISPHENOID
(Posterior cranial fossa)
Anterior limb of anterior semicircular canal

CHAPTER 6

Sagittal Tomograms and Drawn Sections

Figure 6.1 Orientation of Sections

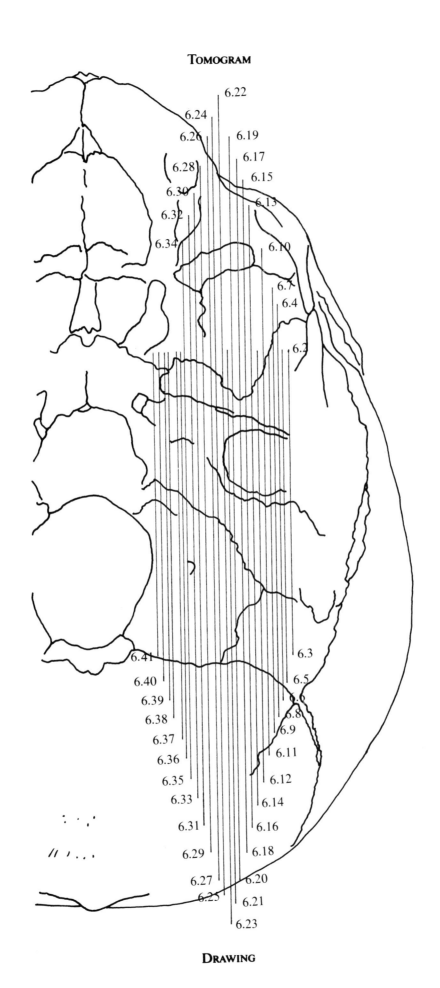

Figure 6.2

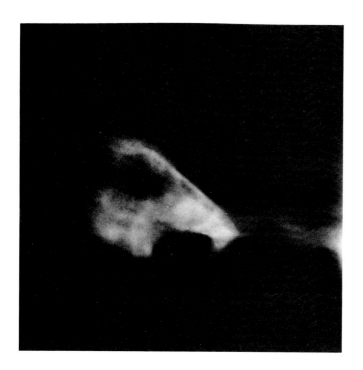

Tomogram

6.2

6.3

Drawing

In this tomogram, matching anatomical Figure 7.3, the cancellous posterior portion of the PETROSAL appears relatively lucent. The tympanic cavity is less sharply marginned, and the tegmen appears irregularly thickened. The MALLEUS and INCUS are dense masses, well demarcated from each other.

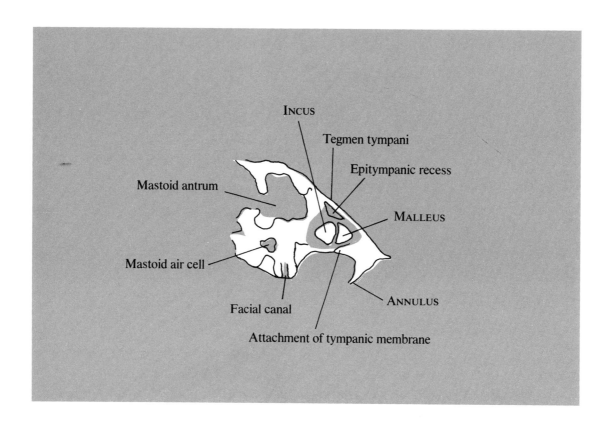

INCUS

Tegmen tympani

Epitympanic recess

Mastoid antrum

MALLEUS

Mastoid air cell

ANNULUS

Facial canal

Attachment of tympanic membrane

Figure 6.3

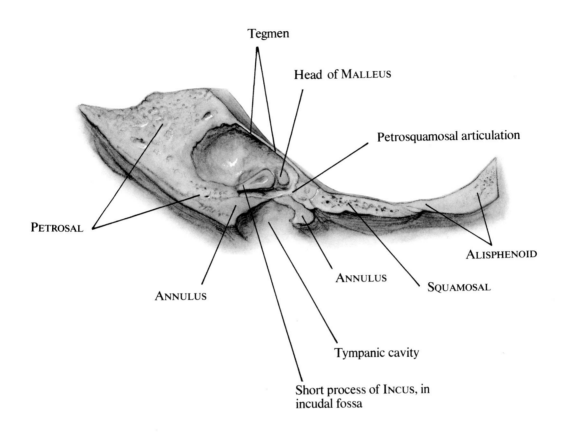

This most lateral of the anatomical sections demonstrates an essentially uniform cancellous mass of the PETROSAL about the comparatively smoothly marginned mastoid portion of the tympanic cavity. The tegmen is thin.

The petrosquamosal suture is seen at the anterior extent of the tympanic cavity.

The SQUAMOSAL is sectioned through the medial portion of the mandibular joint.

The ANNULUS is sectioned through its anterior and posterior portions.

The head of the MALLEUS articulates with the body of the INCUS. The short process of the INCUS rests in the incudal fossa.

Figure 6.4

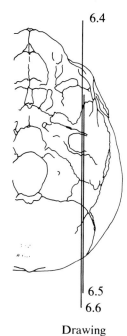

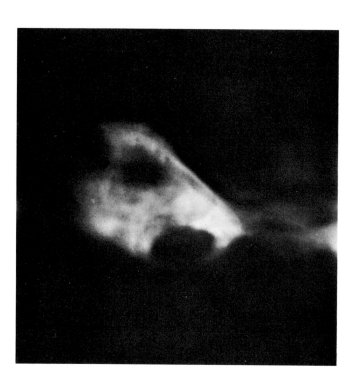

In this tomogram, the lucency of the mastoid antrum is extended into adjacent cancellous bone of the PETROSAL inferior to the antrum.

The tomogram shows the posterior limb of the lateral semicircular canal and a portion of the facial canal.

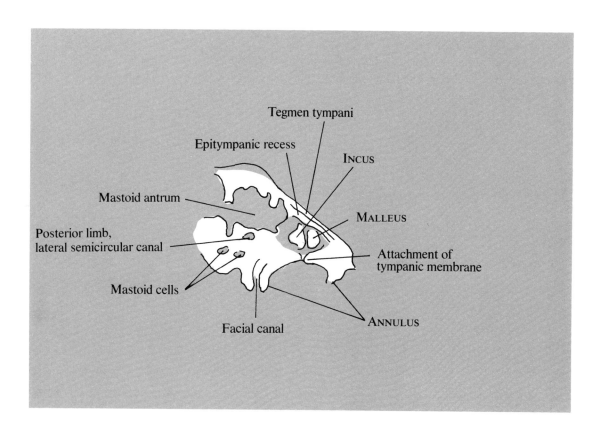

110

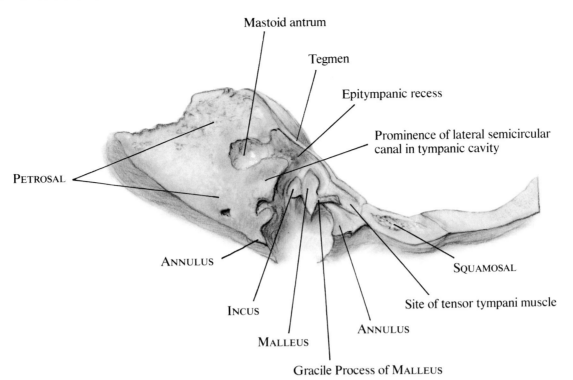

Mastoid antrum

Tegmen

Epitympanic recess

Prominence of lateral semicircular
canal in tympanic cavity

PETROSAL

ANNULUS

SQUAMOSAL

Site of tensor tympani muscle

INCUS

ANNULUS

MALLEUS

Gracile Process of MALLEUS

Figure 6.5

The mastoid antrum of the tympanic cavity approxi-mates the cancellous superior-posterior portion of the PETROSAL.

The petrosquamosal suture is at the anterior margin of the tegmen.

The anterior portion of the ANNULUS is triangular in section. The posterior portion is grossly fused with the PETROSAL.

The body of the MALLEUS closely approximates the long process of the INCUS. The slender gracile pro-cess of the MALLEUS is found in infants; it is usually not evident in tomograms. The chamber anterior to the MALLEUS is the site of the tensor tympani mus-cle.

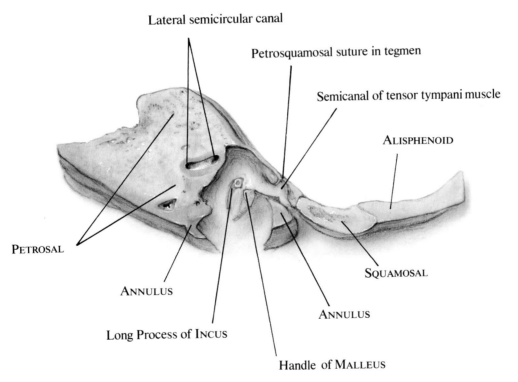

Lateral semicircular canal

Petrosquamosal suture in tegmen

Semicanal of tensor tympani muscle

ALISPHENOID

PETROSAL

SQUAMOSAL

ANNULUS

ANNULUS

Long Process of INCUS

Handle of MALLEUS

Figure 6.6

The lateral portion of the lateral semicircular canal is marginned by dense bone which is well distinguished from the adjacent cancellous bone of the PETROSAL. The petrosquamosal suture is within the tegmen and its inferior margin protrudes as a ridge into the tympanic cavity. The semicanal of the tensor tympani muscle approximates the tegmen portion of the SQUAMOSAL.

The ossicles are sectioned through the handle of the MALLEUS and the long process of the INCUS.

Figure 6.7

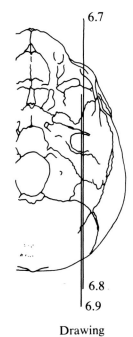

Drawing

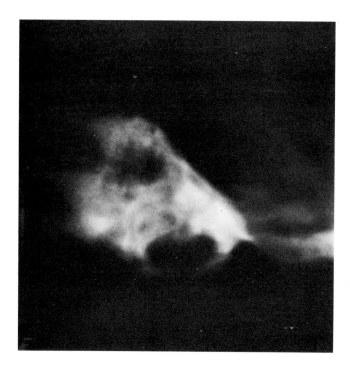

In comparison with the anatomical section of Figure 6.6, this tomogram demonstrates the mastoid antrum and more of the facial canal. It also shows the MALLEUS and the larger portions of INCUS and STAPES, anterior to the oval window.

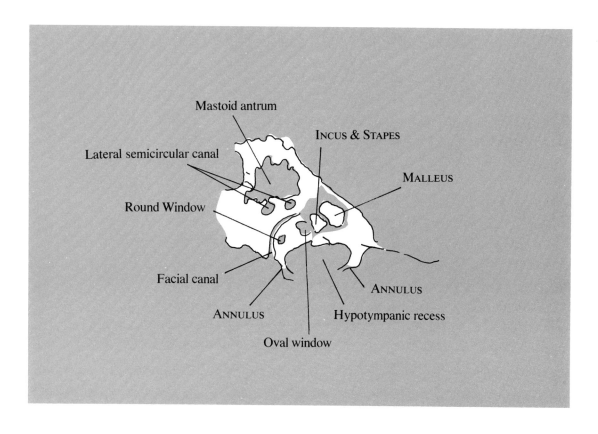

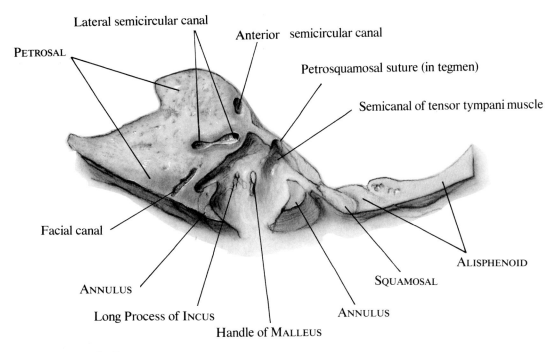

Lateral semicircular canal

Anterior semicircular canal

PETROSAL

Petrosquamosal suture (in tegmen)

Semicanal of tensor tympani muscle

Facial canal

ALISPHENOID

SQUAMOSAL

ANNULUS

ANNULUS

Long Process of INCUS

Handle of MALLEUS

Figure 6.8

This anatomical section demonstrates the lateral semicircular canal, the anterior limb of the anterior semicircular canal and the distal portion of the facial canal. Note that the semicircular canals are distinctly marginned by dense bone.

The semicanal of the tensor tympani muscle approximates the petrosquamosal suture.

The posterior portion of the ANNULUS is incompletely fused with the PETROSAL.

The ossicles are sectioned at the handle of the MALLEUS and the long process of the INCUS.

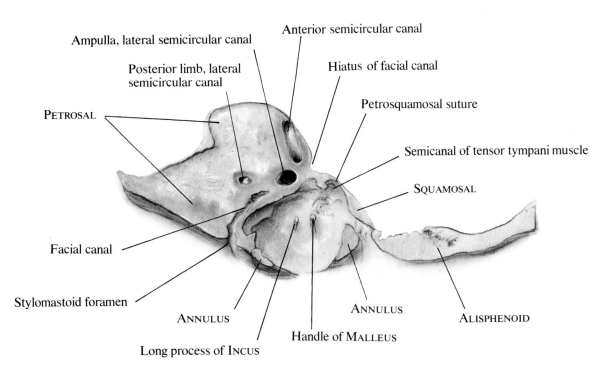

Ampulla, lateral semicircular canal

Anterior semicircular canal

Posterior limb, lateral semicircular canal

Hiatus of facial canal

PETROSAL

Petrosquamosal suture

Semicanal of tensor tympani muscle

SQUAMOSAL

Facial canal

Stylomastoid foramen

ANNULUS

ANNULUS

ALISPHENOID

Handle of MALLEUS

Long process of INCUS

Figure 6.9

The lateral semicircular canal is sectioned through its posterior limb and through its ampulla. The anterior semicircular canal is sectioned through its anterior portion. The hiatus of the facial canal is an indentation on the anterior superior face of the PETROSAL; this is the site of the geniculate ganglion. The distal portion of the facial canal is also shown, to the stylomastoid foramen.

The semicanal of the tensor tympani muscle is adjacent to the tegmen. The semicanal of the stapedius muscle is shown in the posterior wall of the tympanic cavity.

The ossicles are sectioned through the handle of the MALLEUS and the long process of the INCUS.

113

Figure 6.10

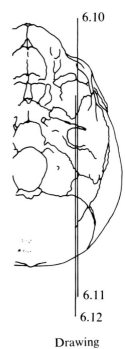

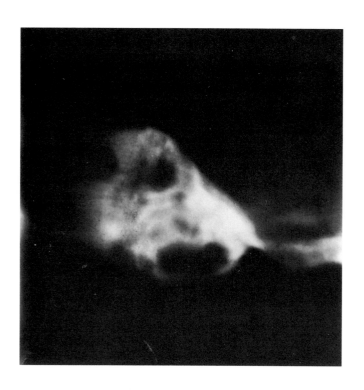

This tomogram corresponds with the anatomical section of Figure 6.11. The subarcuate fosa is much more evident in this tomogram than in the anatomical section.

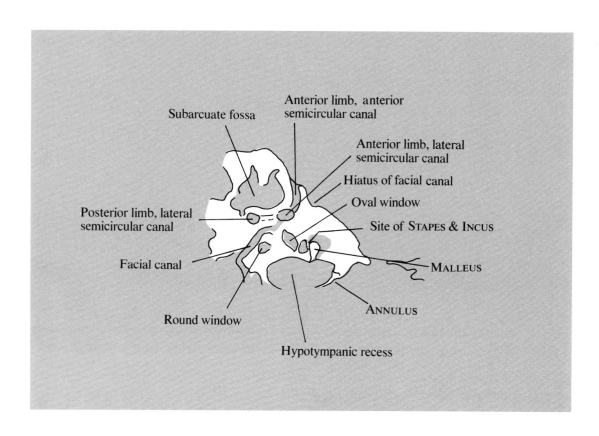

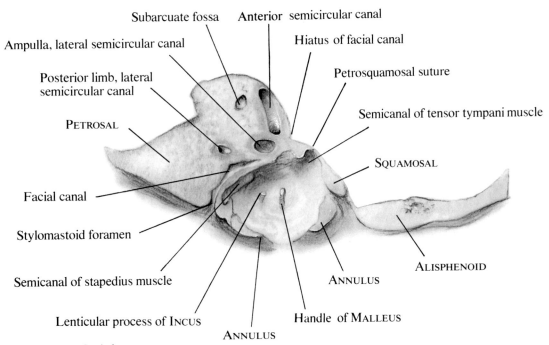

Subarcuate fossa — Anterior semicircular canal

Ampulla, lateral semicircular canal

Hiatus of facial canal

Posterior limb, lateral
semicircular canal

Petrosquamosal suture

PETROSAL

Semicanal of tensor tympani muscle

SQUAMOSAL

Facial canal

Stylomastoid foramen

ALISPHENOID

Semicanal of stapedius muscle

ANNULUS

Lenticular process of INCUS

Handle of MALLEUS

ANNULUS

Figure 6.11

The lateral semicircular canal is sectioned through its posterior limb and ampulla and the anterior semicircular canal through its anterior portion. The margin of the subarcuate fossa is shown. The lateral portion of the facial canal is in much of its length, from its approximation to the ampulla of the lateral semicircu-

lar canal to the stylomastoid foramen.

The semicanal of the tensor tympani muscle approximates the tegmen. The semicanal of the stapedius muscle is partially sectioned in the posterior wall of the tympanic cavity.

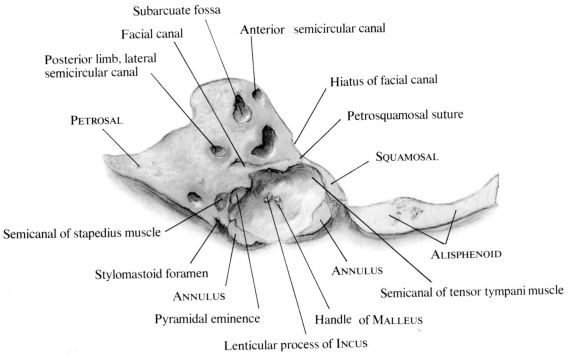

Subarcuate fossa

Facial canal

Anterior semicircular canal

Posterior limb, lateral
semicircular canal

Hiatus of facial canal

PETROSAL

Petrosquamosal suture

SQUAMOSAL

Semicanal of stapedius muscle

ALISPHENOID

Stylomastoid foramen

ANNULUS

ANNULUS

Semicanal of tensor tympani muscle

Pyramidal eminence

Handle of MALLEUS

Lenticular process of INCUS

Figure 6.12

Section demonstrates the common limb and ampullae of the lateral and anterior semicircular canals, the posterior limb of the lateral canal and the superior portion of the anterior canal. The subarcuate fossa is larger than in Figure 6.11. The facial canal is inferior to the common limbs; the medial margin of the hiatus of the canal and of the stylomastoid foramen are also shown.

The semicanal of the tensor tympani muscle is not well demarcated. The semicanal of the stapedius muscle is sectioned in a portion which is almost enclosed; also shown is the pyramidal eminence, around which the tendon of this muscle courses.

The ossicles are sectioned at the handle of the MALLEUS and the lenticular process of the INCUS.

Figure 6.13

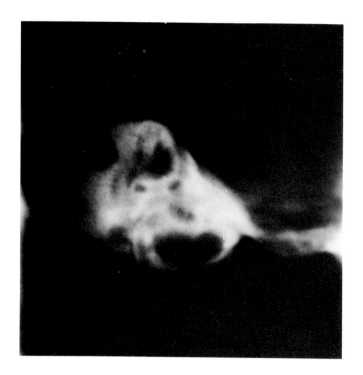

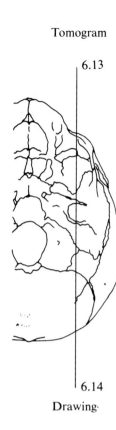

6.14

Drawing·

The subarcuate fossa is prominent in this tomogram. It also shows the lateral limb of the posterior canal and the extent of the anterior limb of the anterior semicircular canal.

The round window is shown in the tomogram but is out of view in the anatomical section.

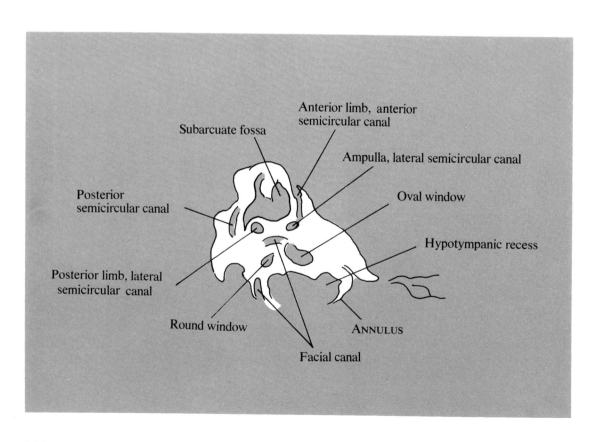

Figure 6.14

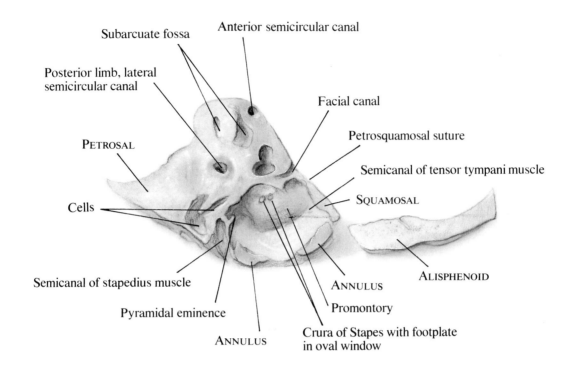

Subarcuate fossa

Anterior semicircular canal

Posterior limb, lateral semicircular canal

Facial canal

PETROSAL

Petrosquamosal suture

Semicanal of tensor tympani muscle

Cells

SQUAMOSAL

Semicanal of stapedius muscle

ALISPHENOID

ANNULUS

Pyramidal eminence

Promontory

ANNULUS

Crura of Stapes with footplate in oval window

This anatomical section is through the common limbs of the lateral and anterior semicircular canals, the posterior limb of the lateral canal and the superior portion of the anterior canal. Two portions of the irregularly contoured subarcuate fossa are exposed.

A short potrion of the facial canal is shown adjacent to its hiatus.

The semicanal of the tensor tympani muscle continues adjacent to the tegmen. In the specimen illustrated, the semicanal of the stapedius muscle penetrates the inferior aspect of the PETROSAL; a thin bony wall is usual. The pyramidal eminence is sectioned. There are irregular lacunae in the PETROSAL posterior to this semicanal; these are probably cells which will be air-containing.

The basal whorl of the cochlea protrudes as the promontory into the tympanic cavity. Superior to it is the oval window containing the footplate of the STAPES; the 2 crura of the STAPES are sectioned.

Figure 6.15

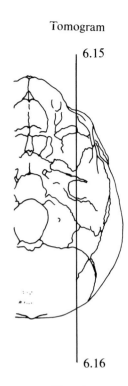

6.15

6.16

Drawing

The semicanals and the facial canal are shown in larger extent in this matching tomogram. It also demonstrates the fossa of the endolymphatic sac.

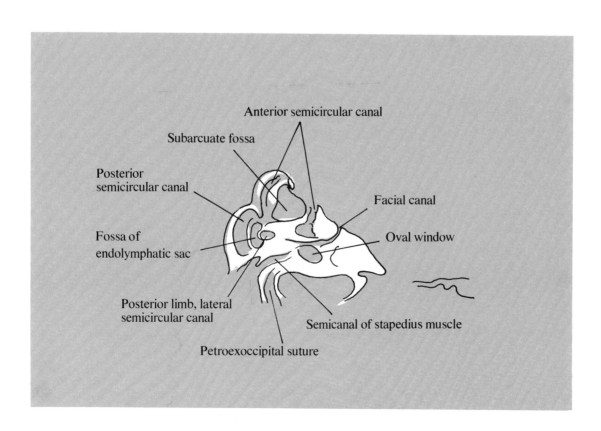

Anterior semicircular canal

Subarcuate fossa

Posterior semicircular canal

Facial canal

Fossa of endolymphatic sac

Oval window

Posterior limb, lateral semicircular canal

Semicanal of stapedius muscle

Petroexoccipital suture

Figure 6.16

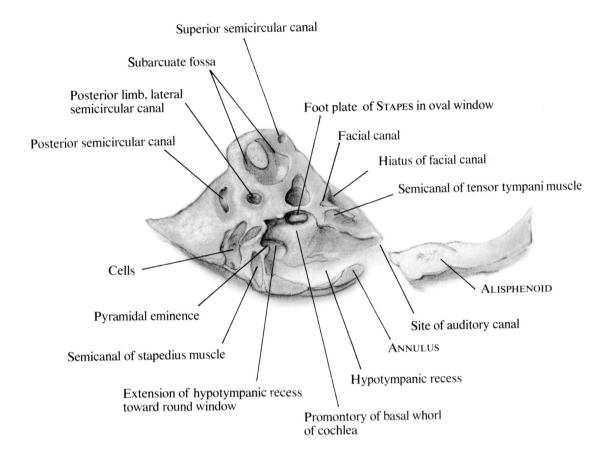

Superior semicircular canal

Subarcuate fossa

Posterior limb, lateral
semicircular canal

Foot plate of STAPES in oval window

Posterior semicircular canal

Facial canal

Hiatus of facial canal

Semicanal of tensor tympani muscle

Cells

ALISPHENOID

Pyramidal eminence

Site of auditory canal

ANNULUS

Semicanal of stapedius muscle

Hypotympanic recess

Extension of hypotympanic recess
toward round window

Promontory of basal whorl
of cochlea

This anatomical section is through the common limb of the lateral and anterior semicircular canals at its junction with the vestibule, through the superior portion of the anterior canal, the posterior limb of the lateral canal and the lateral potrion of the posterior canal. A large portion of the subarcuate fossa is also sectioned.

The facial canal is shown at its hiatus.

The semicanal of the tensor tympani muscle is partially enclosed. The semicanal of the stapedius muscle and its eminence are shown. The cells posterior to this semicanal are exceptionally large in this specimen.

The oval window is shown superior to the promontory. The round window is out of sight in this anatomical section, above the extension of the hypotympanic recess.

Figure 6.17

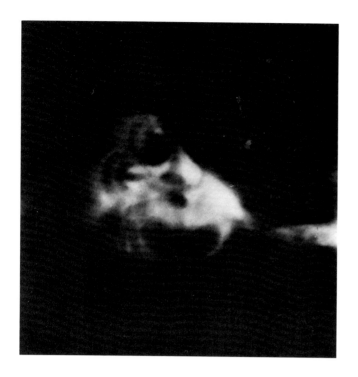

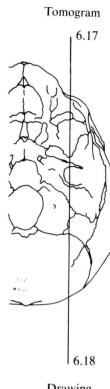

Tomogram

6.17

6.18

Drawing

The tomogram demonstrates a larger extent of the anterior, posterior and lateral semicircular canals. It also shows the rcess of the endolymphatic sac and, less distinctly, the cochlear duct.

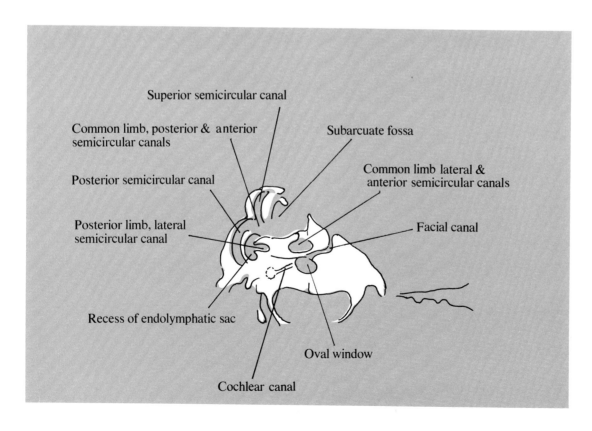

Superior semicircular canal

Common limb, posterior & anterior semicircular canals

Subarcuate fossa

Posterior semicircular canal

Common limb lateral & anterior semicircular canals

Posterior limb, lateral semicircular canal

Facial canal

Recess of endolymphatic sac

Oval window

Cochlear canal

Figure 6.18

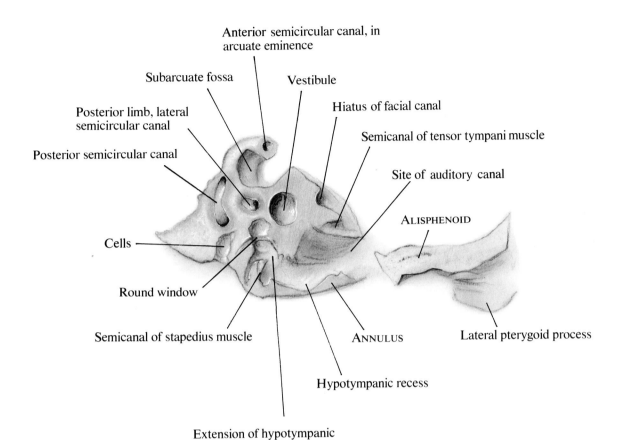

Anterior semicircular canal, in arcuate eminence

Subarcuate fossa

Vestibule

Hiatus of facial canal

Posterior limb, lateral semicircular canal

Semicanal of tensor tympani muscle

Posterior semicircular canal

Site of auditory canal

ALISPHENOID

Cells

Round window

Semicanal of stapedius muscle

ANNULUS

Lateral pterygoid process

Hypotympanic recess

Extension of hypotympanic recess toward round window

The labyrinth is sectioned through the vestibule, the posterior limb of the lateral semicircular canal and the lateral portion of the posterior canal. The superior portion of the anterior semicircular canal is in the lip of the arcuate eminence. The round window is interposed between an extension of the hypotympanic recess and the vestibule.

Open cells are distinguished posterior to the semicanal of the stapedius muscle and inferior to the posterior semicircular canal. In this section these cells extend to the inferior aspect of the PETROSAL.

The facial canal is shown only at its hiatus.

The medial margin of the semicanal of the stapedius is shown. The site of the auditory canal is indicated at its junction with the tympanic cavity and inferior to the semicanal of the tensor tympani muscle.

Figure 6.19

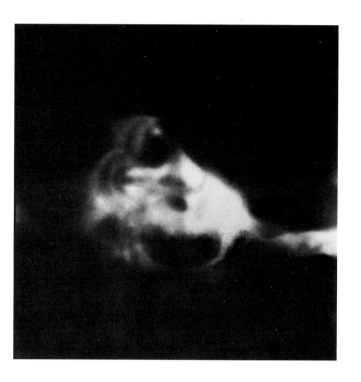

6.20
6.21

Drawing

The corresponding tomogram shows the semicircular canals and the facial canal in greater extent. It also demonstrates the recess of the endolymphatic sac and the cochlea, which are out of the plane of this anatomical section.

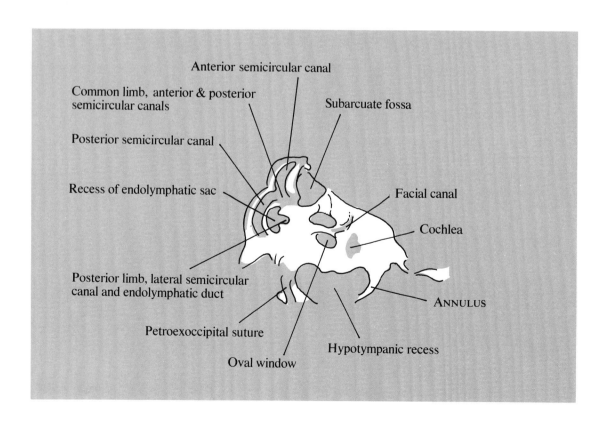

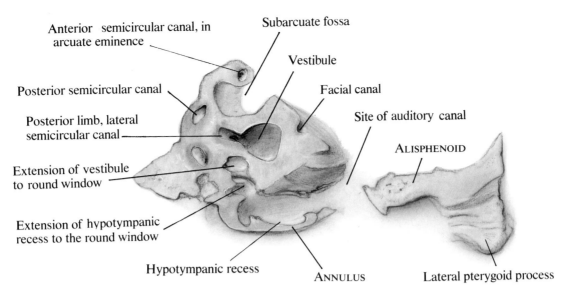

Anterior semicircular canal, in arcuate eminence

Subarcuate fossa

Posterior semicircular canal

Vestibule

Facial canal

Posterior limb, lateral semicircular canal

Site of auditory canal

ALISPHENOID

Extension of vestibule to round window

Extension of hypotympanic recess to the round window

Hypotympanic recess

ANNULUS

Lateral pterygoid process

Figure 6.20

The labyrinth is anatomically sectioned through the vestibule, the junction of the posterior limb of the lateral semicircular canal with the vestibule, the superior and inferior limbs of the posterior semicircular canal, and the superior portion of the anterior semicircular canal. The latter is in the lip of the arcuate eminence.

The round window is shown in its relation to the vestibule and to an extension of the hypotympanic recess. The semicanal of the tensor tympani muscle is only slightly demarcated superior to the site of the musculotubal canal.

The ANNULUS is sectioned at its inferior portion.

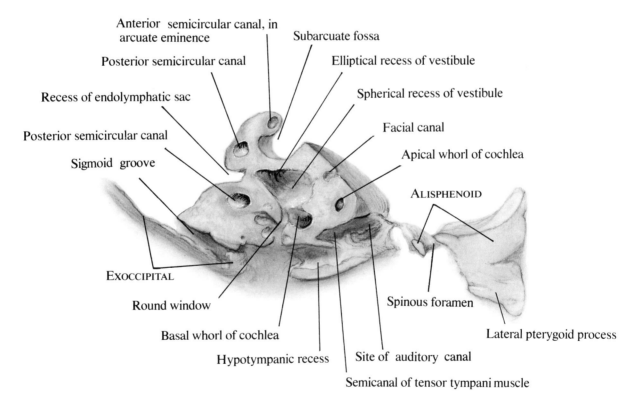

Anterior semicircular canal, in arcuate eminence

Subarcuate fossa

Posterior semicircular canal

Elliptical recess of vestibule

Recess of endolymphatic sac

Spherical recess of vestibule

Posterior semicircular canal

Facial canal

Sigmoid groove

Apical whorl of cochlea

ALISPHENOID

EXOCCIPITAL

Round window

Spinous foramen

Lateral pterygoid process

Basal whorl of cochlea

Hypotympanic recess

Site of auditory canal

Semicanal of tensor tympani muscle

Figure 6.21

Section includes the vestibule, the basal whorl of the cochlea, and the superior portion of the anterior semicircular canal. The superior and inferior limbs of the posterior semicircular canal are on either side of the endolymphatic sac recess.

The round window is at the confluence of the vestibule and the basal whorl. The medial margin of the apical

whorl is also in this plane.

The semicanal of the tensor tympani muscle is demarcated by a transverse ridge from the auditory canal and from the hypotympanic recess.

The sigmoid groove separates the EXOCCIPITAL from the PETROSAL.

123

Figure 6.22

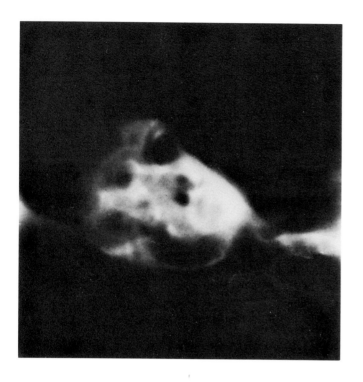

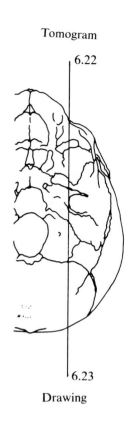

Tomogram

6.22

6.23

Drawing

In comparison with anatomical Figure 6.23, the tomogram further demonstrates the common limb of the anterior and posterior semicircular canals. It also shows the recess of the endolymphatic sac extending into the area between the limbs of the posterior canal.

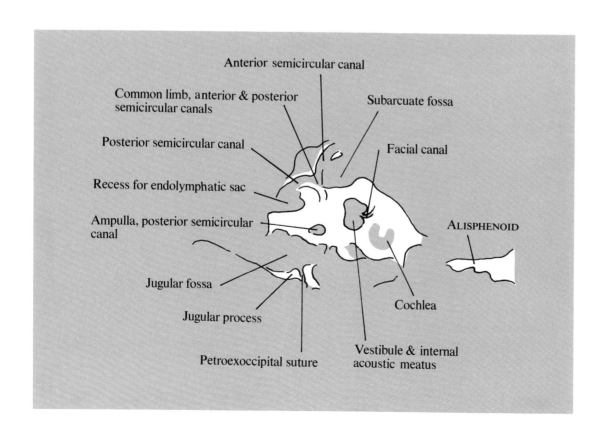

Figure 6.23

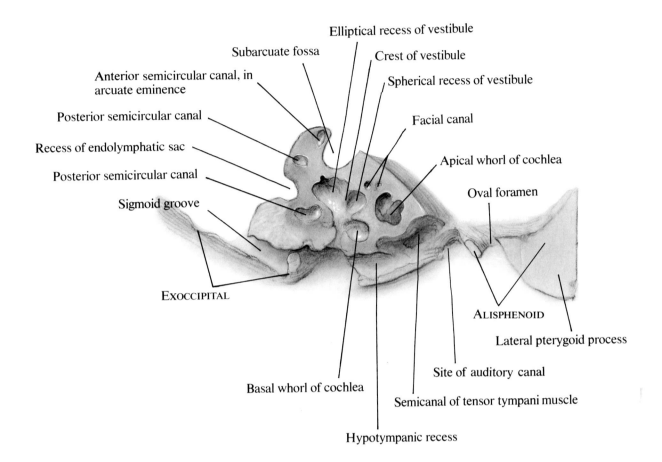

Elliptical recess of vestibule

Subarcuate fossa

Crest of vestibule

Anterior semicircular canal, in arcuate eminence

Spherical recess of vestibule

Posterior semicircular canal

Facial canal

Recess of endolymphatic sac

Apical whorl of cochlea

Posterior semicircular canal

Oval foramen

Sigmoid groove

EXOCCIPITAL

ALISPHENOID

Lateral pterygoid process

Site of auditory canal

Basal whorl of cochlea

Semicanal of tensor tympani muscle

Hypotympanic recess

The portions of the labyrinth exposed in this anatomical section include the vestibule and the basal and apical whorls of the cochlea. The superior portion of the anterior semicircular canal, in the arcuate eminence. And the superior and inferior limbs of the posterior semicircular canal; the inferior limb is close to its ampulla, at its junction with the vestibule.

The curved medial portion of the facial canal is sectioned in two places, superior to the cochlea.

The area of the auditory canal lies between the PETROSAL and the ALISPHENOID encloses the oval foramen.

Figure 6.24

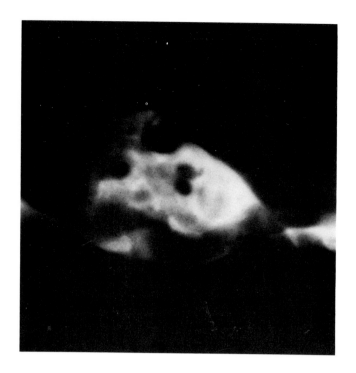

Tomogram

6.24

6.25

Drawing

This tomogram, matching Figure 6.25, demonstrates a greater extent of the superior and posterior semicircular canals. It also demonstrates radiographic overlapping of the internal acoustical meatus and vestibule.

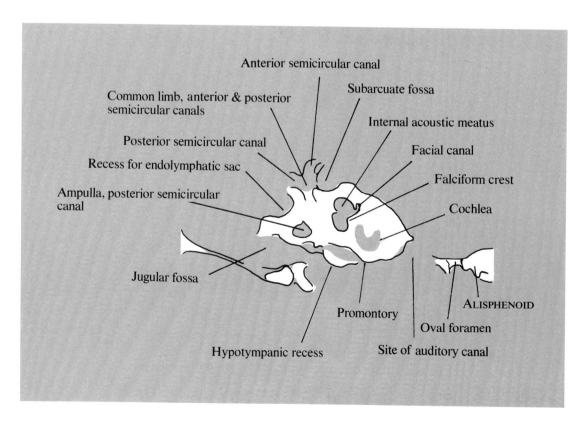

Figure 6.25

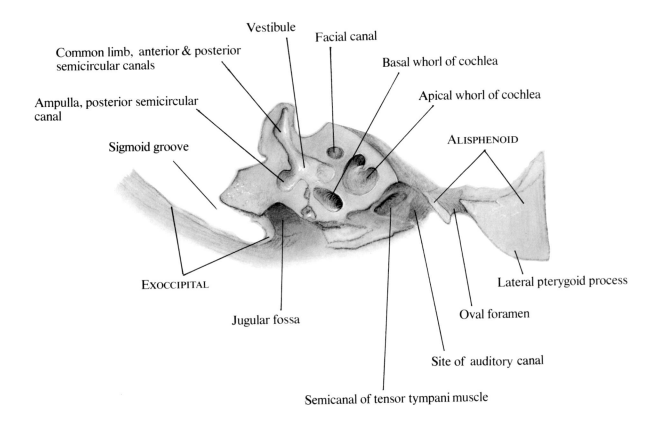

Vestibule

Facial canal

Common limb, anterior & posterior
semicircular canals

Basal whorl of cochlea

Ampulla, posterior semicircular
canal

Apical whorl of cochlea

ALISPHENOID

Sigmoid groove

EXOCCIPITAL

Lateral pterygoid process

Jugular fossa

Oval foramen

Site of auditory canal

Semicanal of tensor tympani muscle

This anatomical section demonstrates the ampulla at the junction of its inferior limb of the posterior semicircular canal with the vestibule, and the common limb of the posterior and anterior canals, at their junction with the vestibule.

The cochlea is sectioned through its basal and apical whorls. The facial canal, superior to the vestibule, is of larger diameter than its more distal portions.

The subarcuate fossa and the recess of the endolymphatic sac are shallow.

The sigmoid groove separates the EXOCCIPITAL and the PETROSAL. The ALISPHENOID encloses the oval foramen. The lateral pterygoid process is sectioned in its greatest sagittal diameters.

Figure 6.26

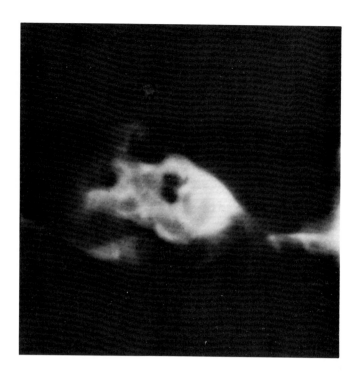

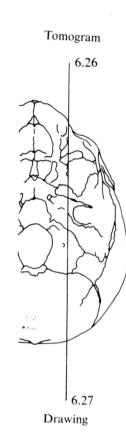

Tomogram

6.26

6.27

Drawing

The tomogram additionally shows the junction of the internal acoustic meatus with the facial canal. And also the common limb of the posterior and anterior semicircular canals; the latter is in the posterior portion of the arcuate eminence.

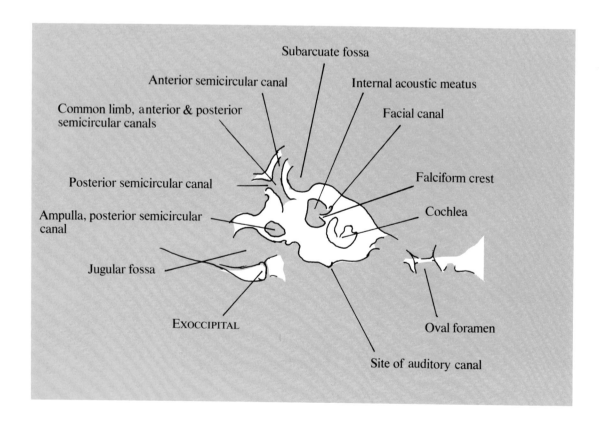

128

Figure 6.27

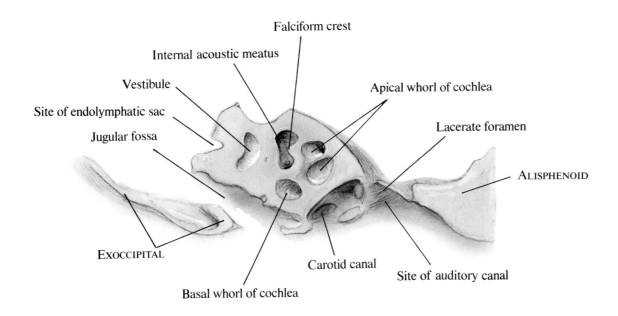

Falciform crest

Internal acoustic meatus

Vestibule

Apical whorl of cochlea

Site of endolymphatic sac

Lacerate foramen

Jugular fossa

ALISPHENOID

EXOCCIPITAL

Carotid canal

Site of auditory canal

Basal whorl of cochlea

In this anatomical section, the labyrinth is represented by the medial margin of the vestibule and by the basal and apical whorls of the cochlea. This is also the plane of the lateral extent of the internal acoustic meatus; the falciform crest intrudes from its anterior margin.

The jugular fossa penetrates inferiorly between the PERIOTIC and the EXOCCIPITAL.

The carotid canal penetrates the PETROSAL from inferior, immediately posterior to the lacerated foramen.

Figure 6.28

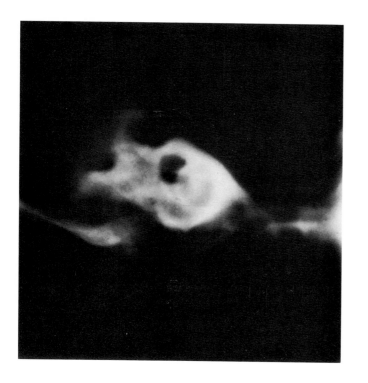

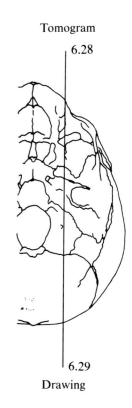

Tomogram
6.28

6.29
Drawing

The tomogram corresponding to Figure 6.29 additionally demonstrates radiographic continuity of the internal acoustic meatus and the cochlea. It also shows the posterior portion of the arcuate eminence.

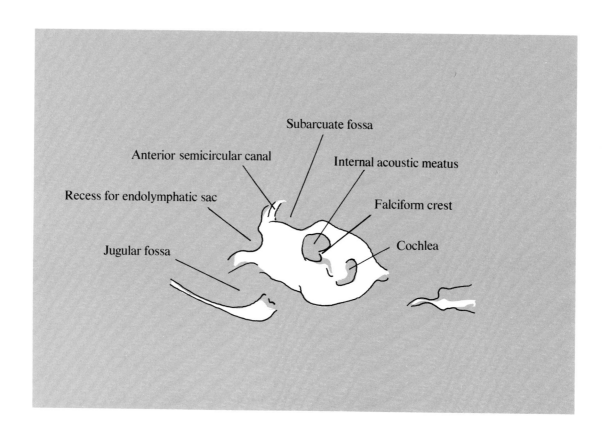

Subarcuate fossa

Anterior semicircular canal

Internal acoustic meatus

Recess for endolymphatic sac

Falciform crest

Jugular fossa

Cochlea

Figure 6.29

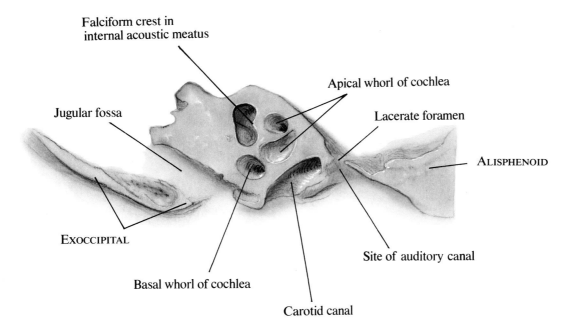

Falciform crest in
internal acoustic meatus

Apical whorl of cochlea

Jugular fossa

Lacerate foramen

ALISPHENOID

EXOCCIPITAL

Site of auditory canal

Basal whorl of cochlea

Carotid canal

This anatomical section demonstrates the basal and apical whorls of the cochlea, and the internal acoustic meatus.
The subarcuate fossa is shallow. The recess of the endolymphatic sac is at its greatest depth.

Figure 6.30

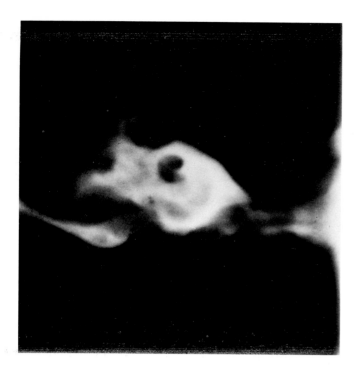

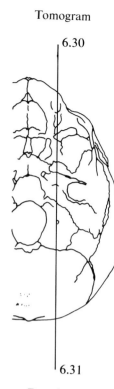

6.30

6.31

Drawing

In comparison with the anatomical Figure 6.31, the tomogram additionally demonstrates the posterior portion of the arcuate eminence, enclosing the superior semicircular canal, and a greater extent of the recess of the endolymphatic sac, on the posterior face of PETROSAL.

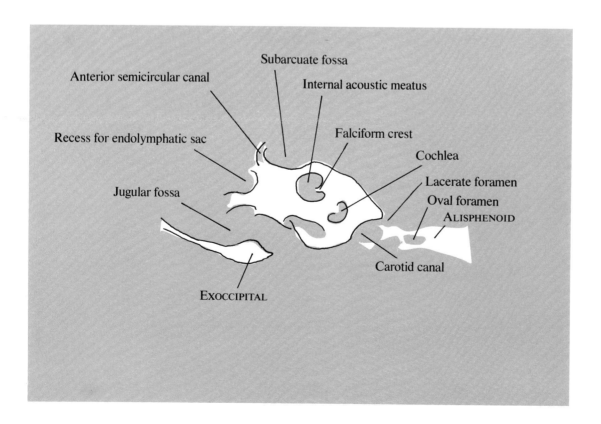

132

Figure 6.31

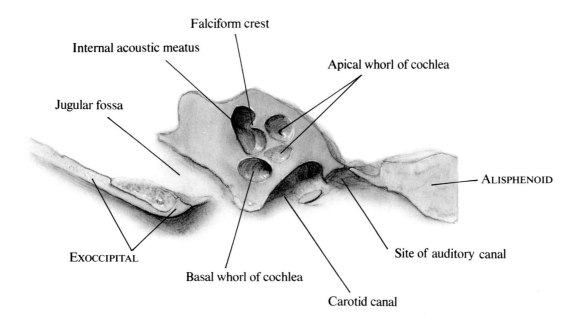

Falciform crest

Internal acoustic meatus

Apical whorl of cochlea

Jugular fossa

ALISPHENOID

EXOCCIPITAL

Site of auditory canal

Basal whorl of cochlea

Carotid canal

The basal and apical whorls of the cochlea approximate the internal acoustic meatus.

The carotid canal and the anditory canal are adjacent, separated skeletally by processes of the ALISHENOID and the PETROSAL.

Figure 6.32

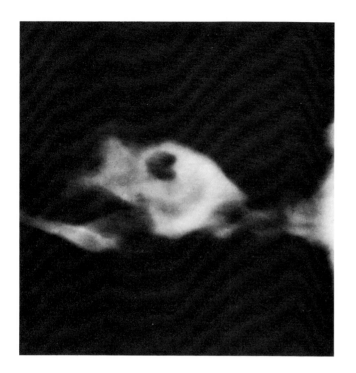

This tomogram is comparable to the anatomical section of Figure 6.33. The falciform crest is well distinguished in the internal acoustic meatus. The anterior enclosure of the carotid canal by the PETROSAL and the ALISPHENOID is indistinct.

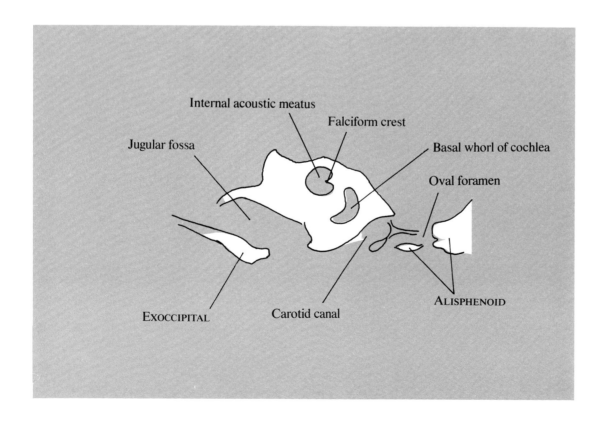

Figure 6.33

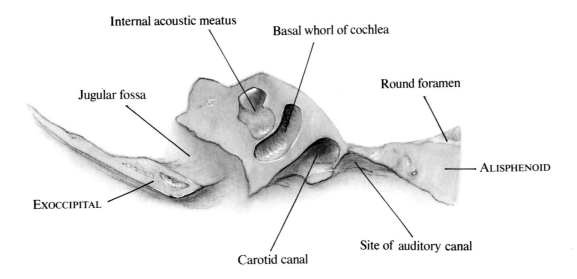

Internal acoustic meatus

Basal whorl of cochlea

Round foramen

Jugular fossa

ALISPHENOID

EXOCCIPITAL

Site of auditory canal

Carotid canal

The cochlea is represented only by its basal whorl, which is separated by a thin plate from the internal acoustic meatus. The ALISPHENOID joins the PETROSAL at suture, superior to the site of the auditory canal. The round foramen penetrates the ALISPHENOID in posteroanterior direction.

Figure 6.34

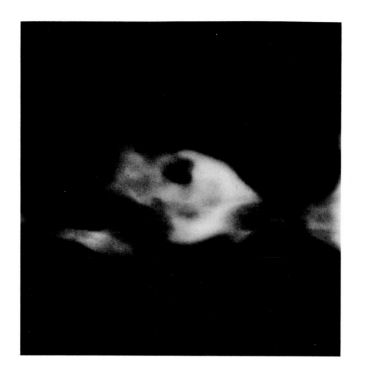

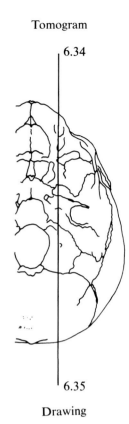

Tomogram

6.34

6.35

Drawing

This tomogram corresponds closely with the anatomy of Figure 6.35.

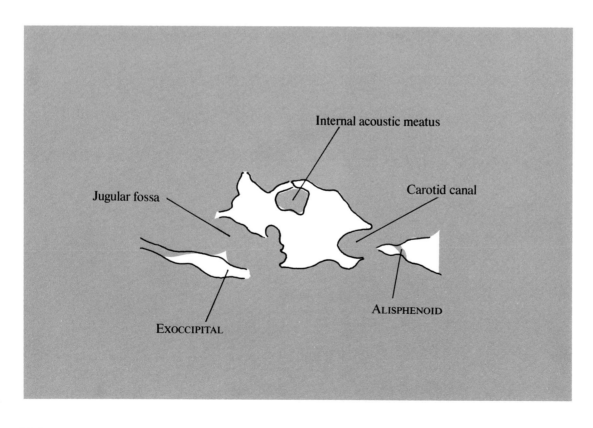

Figure 6.35

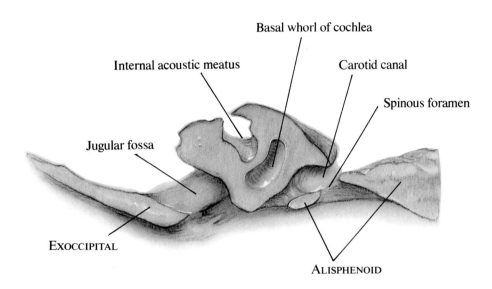

Basal whorl of cochlea

Internal acoustic meatus

Carotid canal

Spinous foramen

Jugular fossa

EXOCCIPITAL

ALISPHENOID

The internal acoustic canal opens in the posterior face of the
PETROSAL. The medial portion of the basal whorl is sepa-
rated from the meatus by a thick layer of dense bone.
The carotid canal is partially enclosed inferiorly.

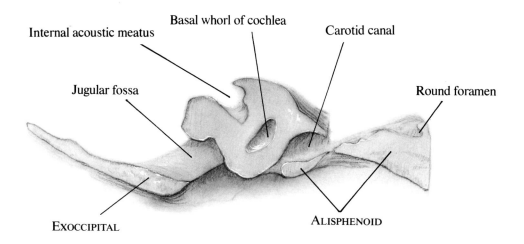

Figure 6.36

The basal whorl of the cochlea is a shallow depression in this section.
Only the outer portion of the internal acoustic is seen.
The carotid canal is enclosed between the PETROSAL and the ALISPHENOID. The posterior portion of the round foramen is seen in the ALISPHENOID.

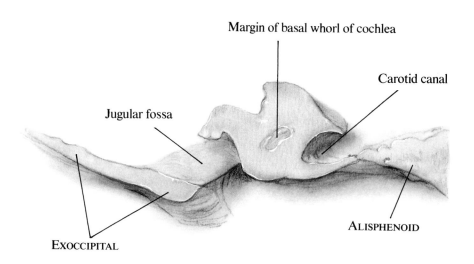

Figure 6.37

The margin of the basal whorl is discernable in the PETROSAL. The internal acoustic meatus is an angular indentation upon its posterior face.
The carotid canal is enclosed by the PETROSAL except on its lateral aspect.

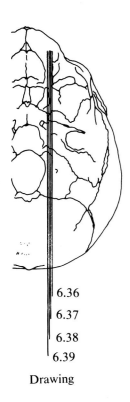

6.36
6.37
6.38
6.39

Drawing

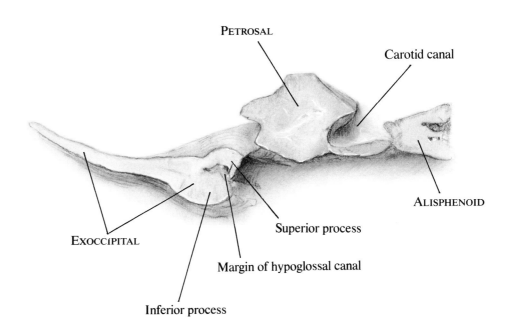

PETROSAL

Carotid canal

ALISPHENOID

Superior process

Margin of hypoglossal canal

EXOCCIPITAL

Inferior process

Figure 6.38

The PETROSAL is sectioned in its pyramidal portion. The bone is almost uniformly cancellous.

The medial margin of the jugular fossa is in view. The adjacent portion of the EXOCCIPITAL is divided into a superior and inferior process, with the margin of the hypoglossal canal between them.

The carotid canal indents the anterior margin of the PETROSAL.

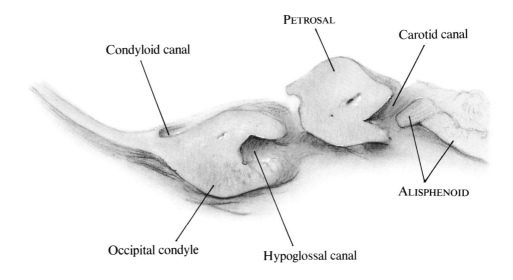

PETROSAL

Carotid canal

Condyloid canal

ALISPHENOID

Occipital condyle

Hypoglossal canal

Figure 6.39

The superior and inferior processes of the EXOCCIPITAL are distinguished by the hypoglossal canal. The occipital condyle is a distinct protrusion upon the inferior aspect of the inferior process.

The carotid indents the PETROSAL less than in Figure 6.38.

Figure 6.40

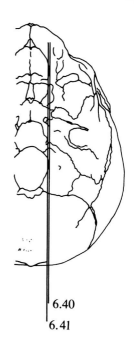

6.40
6.41

Drawing

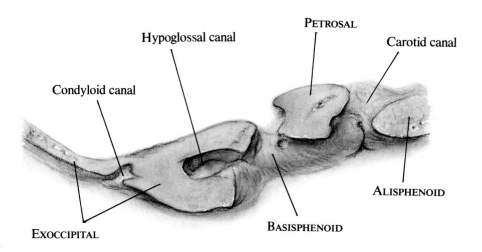

PETROSAL

Hypoglossal canal

Carotid canal

Condyloid canal

ALISPHENOID

EXOCCIPITAL

BASISPHENOID

This is the apex of the pyramidal portion of PETROSAL.
The variable condyloid canal is well shown in the EXOC-
CIPITAL.

Figure 6.41

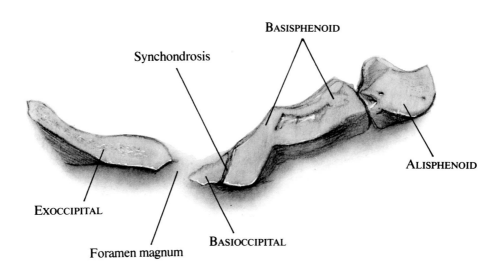

The BASISPHENOID and BASIOCCIPITAL are the median masses of the basicranium. The margin of the foramen magnum is seen between tthe BASIOCCIPITAL and the EXOCCIPITAL.

Selected Bibliography

Anatomy of the Cranium, Human Fetus and Infant

Bosma, J. F. (Ed.) *Symposium on Development of the Basicranium,* Washington, Government Printing Office,1977. Available from Superintendent of Documents as #017–047–00011–6.

Crelin, E. S.: *Anatomy of the Newborn: An Atlas,* Philadelphia, Lea & Febiger, 1969.

Elias, H.: *Basic Human Anatomy as Seen in the Fetus,* St. Louis, Green, 1971.

Nañagas, J. C.: A comparison of the growth of the body dimensions of anencephalic human fetuses with normal fetal growth as determined by graphic analysis and empirical formulae, *Am. J. Anat.,* 35:455–494, 1925.

Parke, W. W.: *Photographic Atlas of Fetal Anatomy,* Baltimore, University Park Press, 1974.

Radiograhy of the Cranium, Human Fetus and Infant

Berkvens, Th.: Radiography of the fetal skull, *Acta. Radiol.,* 34:250–252, 1950.

Caffey, J.: *Pediatric X-Ray Diagnosis,* 6th Edit. Chicago, Medical Publishers, 1973.

Chasler, C. N.: Atlas of Roentgen Anatomy of the Newborn and Infant Skull, St. Louis, Green, 1972.

Krogman, W. M. and Chung, D.: The craniofacial skelton at the age of one month, *The Angle Orthodontist,* 35: 305–310, 1965.

Tomography and Other Techniques of Sectional Radiography

Gordon, R., Herman, G. T. and Johnson, S. A.: Image reconstruction from projections. *Scientific American,* 233:56–68, 1975.

Ledley, R. S., DiChiro, G., Luessenhop, A. J. and Twigg, H. L.: Computerized transaxial x-ray tomography of the human body, *Science,* 186: 210–215, 1974.

New, P. J. F. and Scott, W. R.: Computed Tomography of the Brain and Orbit (EMI Scanning), Baltimore, Williams and Wilkins, 1975.

Prewitt, J.: Prospective methodological advances in radiologic demonstration of the basicranium, In Bosma, J. F. (Ed.) *Symposium on Development of Basicranium,* Washington, Government Printing Office, 1977. Available from Superintendent of Documents as #017–047–00011–6.

Robinson, A. L.: Image Reconstruction (II): Computerized Scanner Explosion, *Science,* 190:647 and 710, 1975. 1975.

Webber, R. L.: Prospective methodological advances in radiologic demonstration of the basicranium, In Bosma, J. F. (Ed.) *Symposium on Development of the Basicranium,* Washington, Government Printing Office, 1977.

Tomography of the Cranium, Human Adult

Berrett, A. Brunner, S. and Valvassori, G. E. *Modern Thin-Section Tomography,* Springfield, Thomas, 1973.

Binet E. F., and Moro, J. J.: A tomographic study of the base of the skull, *Med. Radiog. and Photog.,* 48:30–35, 1972.

Brunner, S., Petersen, O. and Stoksted, P.: Laminagraphy of the temporal bone, *Am. J. Roentgenol.* 86:281–291, 1961.

Daves, M. L. and Loechel, E.: *The Interpretation of Tomograms of the Head, An Atlas,* Springfield, Thomas, 1962.

Etter, L. E.: *Atlas of Roentgen Anatomy of the Skull,* Springfield, Thomas, 1970.

Fischgold, H., David, M. and Bregeat, P.: *La Tomographie de la Base Du Crane En Neuro-Chirurgie et Neuro-Opthalmologie,* Paris, Masson, 1952.

Jensen, J. and Rovsing, H.; (Ed's.) *Fundamentals of Ear Tomography,* Springfield, Thomas, 1971.

Francois, J. and Barrois, J. J.: Anatomie tomographique de l'os temporal normal. *Annales de radiologie,* 2:71–98, 1959.

Holvey, E. H., Rosenthal, L. M. and Anson, B. J.: Tomography of the skull, *Radiology,* 44:425–448, 1945.

Potter, G. D.: *Sectional Anatomy and Tomography of the Head,* New York, Grune & Stratton, 1971.

Valvassori, G. and Buckingham, R. A.: Tomography and Cross Sections of the Ear, Philadelphia, Saunders, 1974.

Valvassori, G. E. and Pierce, R. H.: The normal internal auditory canal, *Am. J. of Roentgenol.*, 92:1232, 1974.

Tomography of the Cranium, Human Infant and Child

Altmann, F.: Congenital atresia of the ear in man and animals, *Ann. Otol., Rhin, and Laryng.* 64:824–858, 1955.

Brunner, S.: Radiological examination of temporal bone in infants and children, *Radiology,* 82:401–406, 1964.

Jensen, J.: Malformation of the inner ear in deaf children, *Acta Radiol.* (Stockh.), Suppl.; 286:11–95; 1969.

Jensen, J. and Rovsing, H.: Tomography in congenital malformation of the middle ear, *Radiology,* 90:268–275, 1968.

Naunton, R. F. and Valvassori, G. E.: Inner ear anomalies: their association with atresia, *Laryngoscope,* 78:1041–49, 1968.

Anatomical Index

The bones which are separate in the term infant are listed in the composite within which they will be united during postnatal development. Thus, the BASIOCCIPITAL, EXOCCIPITAL and SUPRAOCCIPITAL are listed in the OCCIPITAL composite. The BASISPHENOID, ALISPHENOID and PTERGYGOID in the SPHENOID composite. The NASAL SEPTUM and INFERIOR CONCHA in the ETHMOID composite. The PETROSAL, SQUAMOSAL and ANNULUS in the TEMPORAL composite. The MALLEUS, INCUS and STAPES are listed as OSSICLES.

146

☆ U.S. GOVERNMENT PRINTING OFFICE : 1978 O—257-231